Academic VOCABULARY Toolkit

Mastering High-Use Words for Academic Achievement

Dr. Kate Kinsella

with Theresa Hancock

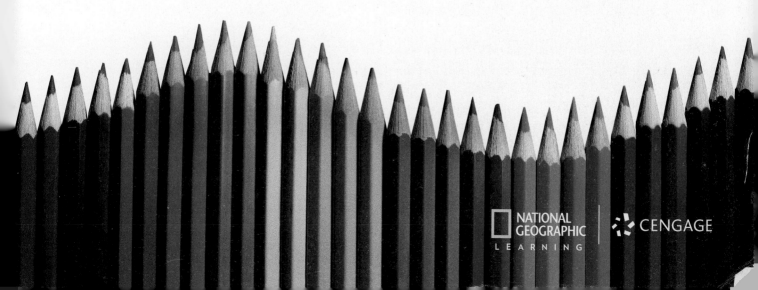

NATIONAL GEOGRAPHIC LEARNING | CENGAGE

Acknowledgments

Grateful acknowledgment is given to the authors, artists, photographers, museums, publishers, and agents for permission to reprint copyrighted material. Every effort has been made to secure the appropriate permission. If any omissions have been made or if corrections are required, please contact the Publisher.

Photo credits

Wrap cover ©Victoria Ivanova/500px Prime. **Front cover** (c) ©Yurchenko Yevhenii/Shutterstock **iv** (tl) Bokan/Shutterstock.com. (cr) Sashkin/Shutterstock.com. (cl) Sebastian Kaulitzki/Shutterstock.com. (br) Weerasak saeku/Shutterstock.com.

Acknowledgments and credits continue on page 180.

For product information and technology assistance, contact us at **Customer & Sales Support, 888-915-3276**

For permission to use material from this text or product, submit all requests online at **www.cengage.com/permissions**
Further permissions questions can be emailed to **permissionrequest@cengage.com**

National Geographic Learning | Cengage
1 Lower Ragsdale Drive
Building 1, Suite 200
Monterey, CA 93940

Cengage Learning is a leading provider of customized learning solutions with employees residing in nearly 40 different countries and sales in more than 125 countries around the world. Find your local representative at **www.cengage.com**.

Visit National Geographic Learning online at **NGL.Cengage.com/school**

ISBN: 9781337296229

Printed in the United States of America
Print Number: 01
Print Year: 2017

Contents
at a Glance

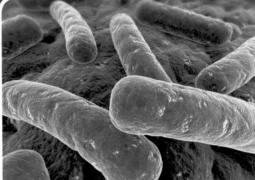

Unit 1
Describe

🏁 SMARTSTART

Unit 2
Analyze Informational Text

🏁 SMARTSTART

Unit 3
Cause and Effect

🏁 SMARTSTART

Unit 4
Sequence

🏁 SMARTSTART

Unit 5
Create

Unit 6
Compare and Contrast

Unit 7
Inference

SMART *START*

Unit 8
Argument

SMART *START*

Toolkit Unit 1 | Describe

Describe

To **describe** a person, explain how he or she looks, acts, and speaks. If possible, include what others think or say about the person.

To **describe** a location or a thing, use your senses to explain how it looks, feels, smells, sounds, and tastes.

 Find It   Read the sentences below and underline the words that **describe** a person, location, or thing.

1. My three-year-old brother makes a mess wherever he goes! His clothes are usually covered in mud, or paint. His face is usually smeared with chocolate or banana or whatever he was last eating. He leaves toys everywhere. But he has a happy smile and big, brown eyes. Sometimes I get annoyed at him for a moment, but then he looks at me with his puppy-dog eyes, and I forgive him!

2. Last summer my family visited a beach in Florida. It was a perfect beach with warm, calm crystal blue water. It had powdery, soft sand that was as white as sugar. The beach was covered with shells and sand dollars. It even had a small snack bar that served hot dogs, burgers, and ice cream. My mother said it was one of the best beaches she'd ever been to.

 Try It   Think about one person you know. Write one important detail in each section of the chart that you would use to **describe** the person.

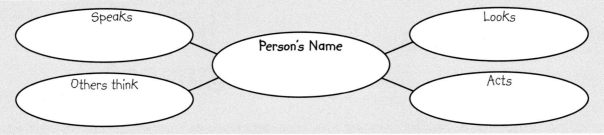

Speaks

Looks

Person's Name

Others think

Acts

RATE WORD KNOWLEDGE

Circle the number that shows your knowledge of the words you'll use to describe people, places, and things.

6th Grade	7th Grade	BEFORE	8th Grade	AFTER
characteristic	explanation	1 2 3 4	clarify	1 2 3 4
explanation	respond	1 2 3 4	symbolize	1 2 3 4
description	unique	1 2 3 4	function	1 2 3 4
accurate	complex	1 2 3 4	feature	1 2 3 4
demonstrate	element	1 2 3 4	coherent	1 2 3 4
feature	attribute	1 2 3 4	description	1 2 3 4

RATE IT

DISCUSSION GUIDE
- Form groups of four.
- Assign letters to each person. Ⓐ Ⓑ
- Each group member takes a turn   Ⓓ Ⓒ
  leading a discussion.
- Prepare to report about one word.

DISCUSS WORDS

Discuss how well you know the eighth grade words. Then, report to the class how you rated each word.

GROUP LEADER **Ask**

So, _____ what do you know
(NAME)

about the word _____ ?

GROUP MEMBERS **Discuss**

1 = I **don't recognize** the word _____ .

I need to learn what it means.

2 = I **recognize** the word _____ ,

but I need to learn the meaning.

3 = I'm **familiar** with the word _____ .

I think it means _____ .

4 = I **know** the word _____ .

It's a _____ , and it means _____ .
(PART OF SPEECH)

Here is my example sentence: _____ .

REPORTER **Report Word Knowledge**

Our group gave the word _____ a rating of _____ because _____ .

SET A GOAL AND REFLECT

First, set a vocabulary goal for this unit by selecting at least three words that you plan to thoroughly learn.
At the end of the unit, return to this page and write a reflection about one word you have mastered.

GOAL

During this unit I plan to thoroughly learn the words _____ ,

_____ , and _____ . Increasing my word knowledge will help

me speak and write effectively when I describe a person, location, or _____ .

As a result of this unit, I feel most confident about the word _____ .

This is my model sentence: _____

_____ .

REFLECTION

clarify

verb

Say it: clar • i • fy

 Write it: _____ **Write it again:** _____

 _____

TOOLKIT

Meaning

to make something easier to understand

Synonyms
- explain

Examples
- The researcher hoped the _____ would **clarify** the results of her experiment.

- The caption beneath the photograph helped **clarify** why the boat was on the _____ .

Forms
- **Present:**

  I/You/We/They   clarify

  He/She/It   clarifies
- **Past:**   clarified

Family
- **Noun:** clarification

Word Partners
- help clarify
- clarify issues/positions

Examples
- New discoveries **help clarify** how humans spread across the globe.
- The reporter asked the candidate to **clarify his position** on tax cuts.

 Try It

Reading the summary helped **clarify** the issues raised (in/on) _____ _____

_____ .

VERBAL PRACTICE

Talk about it

     Discuss Listen Write

Discuss ideas with your partner, listen to classmates, and then write your favorite idea.

1. When you are explaining how to get to the _____ , you can

   clarify your directions by tracing the route on a map.

2. Flight attendants help **clarify** safety procedures for passengers by _____

   _____ .

clarify
verb

WRITING PRACTICE

Collaborate

Discuss
Agree
Write
Listen

Discuss ideas with your partner and agree on the best words to complete the frame. ▶

The new president is _____ his position on _____

by _____ .

Our Turn

Discuss
Listen
Write

Read the prompt. Work with the teacher to complete the frames. Write a thoughtful response that includes a personal experience.

PROMPT: Describe a time when a teacher clarified an issue that needed to be discussed in a specific assignment. What happened after you understood the expectations?

One of the assignments our _____ teacher gave the class was to discuss

the issue of _____ in (a/an) _____

_____ . Many of us struggled until (he/she) _____

_____ the issue for us by _____

_____ . Once we understood the expectations, we were able to

_____ .

Be an Academic Author

Write
Discuss
Listen

Read the prompt and complete the frames. Strengthen your response with a relevant example.

PROMPT: Imagine that several new students recently joined your class. What is an important rule that you might help clarify for your new classmates?

If several new students joined our class, one important school rule I would _____ for

them is the rule about _____ .

It is important that new classmates understand this rule so they know exactly what to

do in case they _____ .

Construct a Response

Write
Discuss
Listen

Read the prompt and brainstorm ideas for a thoughtful response. Construct a response that includes a relevant example. ▶

PROMPT: Think about a topic you're hearing about in the news or learning about in class that is confusing you. What could you do to help clarify the topic?

_____

_____

_____

grammar tip ▶

The **present progressive tense** is formed with *am, is, are* + a verb ending in *-ing*.

EXAMPLE: Americans **are consuming** more chocolate. The dog **is running** down the street.

symbolize
verb

Say it: sym • bol • ize

 Write it: _____   **Write it again:** _____

 _____

TOOLKIT

Meaning to represent something	**Examples** • The gold cross in the flag of _____ **symbolizes** sunlight.

Synonyms • represent	• The skull on Winston's football _____ is meant to **symbolize** his team, the Pirates.

Forms
- **Present:**

I/You/We/They	symbolize
He/She/It	symbolizes

- **Past:** symbolized

Family
- **Nouns:** symbol, symbolism
- **Adjective:** symbolic
- **Adverb:** symbolically

Word Partners
- come to symbolize
- meant to symbolize

Examples
- Ribbons of different colors have **come to symbolize** different causes.
- Cutting a cake at a wedding reception is **meant to symbolize** the bride and groom working together.

 Try It

Stickers or emojis like the _____ are used to **symbolize** certain emotions in text messages.

VERBAL PRACTICE

Talk about it

Discuss
Listen
Write

Discuss ideas with your partner, listen to classmates, and then write your favorite idea.

1. The color red sometimes **symbolizes** _____ .

2. Many people think that _____ has come to **symbolize** the United States.

symbolize

verb

WRITING PRACTICE

Collaborate

Discuss
Agree
Write
Listen

Discuss ideas with your partner and agree on the best words to complete the frame. ▶

People usually wear wristbands to _____ their support for certain causes,

such as _____ .

Our Turn

Discuss
Listen
Write

Read the prompt. Work with the teacher to complete the frames. Write a thoughtful response that includes a relevant example. ▶

PROMPT: **Describe an animal that symbolizes a particular human trait in a story or folktale.**

Animals in certain stories or folktales, such as _____ are

often used to _____ human traits. For example, (a/an) _____

_____ sometimes _____ the human

characteristic of _____ .

Be an Academic Author

Write
Discuss
Listen

Read the prompt and complete the frames. Strengthen your response with a personal experience. ▶

PROMPT: **Explain what you enjoy about a specific holiday. Describe one aspect, such as candles or certain decorations, and what it symbolizes about the event.**

One holiday that I frequently enjoy is _____ because my

_____ .

One aspect that I particularly enjoy is when the _____ .

It _____ the importance of _____

_____ .

Construct a Response

Write
Discuss
Listen

Read the prompt and brainstorm ideas. Construct a thoughtful response that includes a relevant example.

PROMPT: **Imagine that you are going to write a poem about hope and freedom. Describe an object, animal, color, or other image you would include to symbolize hope and freedom, and explain why.**

_____

_____

_____

grammar tip ▶

An **adverb** that tells how many times something happens can go before or after a verb. The adverbs *always, usually, sometimes, often, frequently, typically,* and *never* generally go before the main verb.

EXAMPLE: I **usually** symbolize to an email right away. I **typically** answer the phone on the second ring.

function

noun

Say it: func • tion

 Write it: _____ **Write it again:** _____

 _____

Meaning	**Examples**
the thing something is supposed to do	• One function of the doctor's _____ are to protect her from germs. 
Synonyms	• The primary **function** of a giraffe's long neck is to help it eat _____ from tall trees.
• task; purpose	

TOOLKIT

Forms
• **Singular:** function
• **Plural:** functions

Family
• **Verb:** function
• **Adjectives:** functioning, functional

Word Partners
• primary function of
• perform the function of

Examples
• The **primary function of** a ceiling fan is to cool a room on a hot day
• The vice president will **perform the function of the** president if the president is ill.

 Try It

From my perspective, the primary **function** of a study abroad program is to allow students to

_____ .

VERBAL PRACTICE

Talk about it   Discuss ideas with your partner, listen to classmates, and then write your favorite idea.

Discuss
Listen
Write

1. One **function** of a library is to provide visitors with _____

_____ .

2. The primary **function** of my _____ is to keep me

warm.

WRITING PRACTICE

Collaborate

Discuss
Agree
Write
Listen

Discuss ideas with your partner and agree on the best words to complete the frame. ▶

In our opinion, the primary _____ of _____ education is

to _____ .

Our Turn

Discuss
Listen
Write

Read the prompt. Work with the teacher to complete the frames. Write a thoughtful response that includes a relevant example. ▶
PROMPT: Describe two functions of a cell phone that you think are very important.

From my perspective, two very important _____ of a cell phone are being able to

_____ and _____ .

These are important functions because _____

_____ .

Be an Academic Author

Write
Discuss
Listen

Read the prompt and complete the frames. Strengthen your response with a personal experience.
PROMPT: Imagine that you are trying to build something but you don't have any tools. Describe one thing you might be able to use to perform the function of a tool in order to construct your project.

If I didn't have any tools, I might be able to use a _____ to perform

the _____ of a _____ . It might

be awkward to use, but it would be necessary if I had to build (a/an) _____

_____ .

Construct a Response

Write
Discuss
Listen

Read the prompt and brainstorm ideas for a thoughtful response. Construct a response that includes a relevant example. ▶
PROMPT: The human body is made up of distinct systems, such as the respiratory, nervous, skeletal, or muscular system. Describe the primary function of one system and why it is important.

_____

_____

_____

grammar tip ▶

Adjectives are always singular even if they describe a plural noun. Do not add *-s* to adjectives that describe plural nouns.

EXAMPLE: Several of our **new** neighbors have **loud** dogs and **colorful** cars.

feature

noun

 Write it: _____ **Write it again:** _____

 _____

TOOLKIT

Meaning an important part or a special characteristic	**Examples** • The latest _____ has several new **features** that are sure to make it very popular.
Synonyms • part, quality, aspect	• One **feature** that bacteria has in common with other living _____ is they both have chromosomes.

Forms
- **Singular:** feature
- **Plural:** features

Family
- **Verb:** feature
- **Adjective:** featured

Word Partners
- key feature

- have features in common

Examples
- The beautiful fountain is a **key feature** of the new park.
- Penguins and ducks **have many features** in common, such as webbed feet.

 Try It

My cell phone has several new **features**, including _____ .

VERBAL PRACTICE

Talk about it   Discuss ideas with your partner, listen to classmates, and then write your favorite idea.

Discuss
Listen
Write

1. _____ and _____ have many

   features in common.

2. A key **feature** of mammals is that they _____ .

WRITING PRACTICE

Collaborate

Discuss
Agree
Write
Listen

Discuss ideas with your partner and agree on the best words to complete the frame. ▶

One of the key _____ I would like to have in my future home is (a/an) _____

_____ .

Our Turn

Discuss
Listen
Write

Read the prompt. Work with the teacher to complete the frames. Write a thoughtful response that includes a relevant example. ▶

PROMPT: **Describe two key features that new bands need to have in order to become popular.**

In order to become popular, two key _____ that new bands need to have are

_____ and _____

_____ . These features would help any new band become as

successful as _____ .

Be an Academic Author

Write
Discuss
Listen

Read the prompt and complete the frames. Strengthen your response with relevant examples.

PROMPT: **Describe two animals that have several features in common.** ▶

From my perspective, (a/an) _____ _____ and (a/an) _____

_____ have several _____ in common.

For example, they both have _____ and the ability to

_____ .

Construct a Response

Write
Discuss
Listen

Read the prompt and brainstorm ideas for a thoughtful response. Construct a response that includes a convincing reason. ▶

PROMPT: **Describe two unique features of the planet Earth. Are these features important to the survival of human beings? Explain why or why not.**

_____

_____

_____

grammar tip ▶

Adjectives are always singular even if they describe a plural noun. Do not add **-s** to adjectives that describe plural nouns.

EXAMPLE: My sister and I wore **wild** costumes and **crazy** shoes to our cousins' Halloween party.

coherent

adjective

Say it: co • **her** • ent

Write it: _____   **Write it again:** _____

_____

TOOLKIT

Meaning
clear; easy to follow and understand

Synonyms
• understandable; well-organized

Antonyms
• incoherent

Examples
• My uncle's words were not **coherent** because we had a bad _____ .

• Our tent came with a **coherent** set of _____ for how to set it up.

Family
• **Noun:** coherence
• **Adverb:** coherently

Word Partners
• coherent argument
• coherent (plan, strategy, outline)

Examples
• My parents didn't want me to go on the Quebec trip with my French class, but I made such a **coherent argument** for it, that they finally agreed.
• Writing an organized research paper is easier if you first prepare a **coherent outline**.

 Try It
In order to _____ , a soccer team must work together and develop a **coherent strategy**.

VERBAL PRACTICE

Talk about it   Discuss ideas with your partner, listen to classmates, and then write your favorite idea.

Discuss
Listen
Write

1. The presidential candidate lost support because he had no **coherent** strategy for improving the nation's _____ .

2. My answers on the test were _____ because I was too tired to focus on making a **coherent** argument.

WRITING PRACTICE

Collaborate

Discuss
Agree
Write
Listen

Discuss ideas with your partner and agree on the best words to complete the frame. ▶

If our class were to volunteer to clean up a local park, a _____ plan for the project

would include _____ .

Our Turn

Discuss
Listen
Write

Read the prompt. Work with the teacher to complete the frames. Write a thoughtful response that includes a personal experience. ▶

PROMPT: Describe a coherent argument someone made that helped change your mind about the importance of a school subject.

I used to think _____ was boring and that those skills weren't

useful outside of school. However, my _____ made a very

_____ argument that _____ can

help us to _____ .

Be an Academic Author

Write
Discuss
Listen

Read the prompt and complete the frames. Strengthen your response with a relevant example. ▶

PROMPT: Describe some of the elements of a coherent essay.

Some elements of a _____ essay include a strong _____

_____ , a series of _____ points

backed up by facts, and a strong conclusion. It is also helpful to include transition words like

"however" and " _____ " to move smoothly from

one _____ to another.

Construct a Response

Write
Discuss
Listen

Read the prompt and brainstorm ideas for a thoughtful response. Construct a response that includes a relevant example. ▶

PROMPT: It's hard to listen to someone giving a speech that is rambling, disorganized, or difficult to hear. What are some steps you would take to make sure your next oral presentation is coherent?

_____

_____

_____

grammar tip ▶

The preposition *to* needs to be followed by a verb in the base form.

EXAMPLE: If you want **to improve** your Spanish, you'll have **to practice** with native speakers.

description

noun

Say it: des • **crip** • tion

 Write it: _____ **Write it again:** _____

 _____

Meaning
a spoken or written statement that explains what someone or something is like

Synonyms
- explanation

Examples
- The doctor asked for a **description** of the _____ I was experiencing.

- Our grandmother's vivid **descriptions** of her childhood have always been _____ to us.

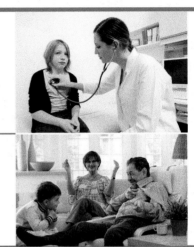

Forms
- **Singular:** description
- **Plural:** descriptions

Family
- **Verb:** describe
- **Adjective:** descriptive

Word Partners
- provide a (detailed/accurate) description
- (lengthy/brief) description

Examples
- The woman **provided such an accurate description** of the thief, that the police sketch looked exactly like him.
- Our science teacher asked each of us for a **brief description** of our science fair projects.

 Try It

Before I played _____ for the first time, my older brother provided a detailed **description** of the different characters I could play.

VERBAL PRACTICE

Talk about it

Discuss
Listen
Write

Discuss ideas with your partner, listen to classmates, and then write your favorite idea.

1. When my _____ went missing, I created a flyer with a detailed **description** and posted it all around the neighborhood.

2. My friend's lengthy **description** of her trip to _____ made me really want to go there.

description

noun

Collaborate

Discuss
Agree
Write
Listen

Discuss ideas with your partner and agree on the best words to complete the frame. ▶

A teacher's _____ of a complex topic, such as _____

_____ , should be detailed and include visual aids.

Our Turn

Discuss
Listen
Write

Read the prompt. Work with the teacher to complete the frames. Write a thoughtful response that includes a relevant example and personal experience. ▶

PROMPT: **Imagine you are writing an online review of a restaurant. What details would you include to provide an accurate description of your experience?**

In order to provide an accurate _____ of the restaurant _____

for an online review, I would mention its _____ and

_____ . It is truly (a/an) _____

_____ place to eat!

Be an Academic Author

Write
Discuss
Listen

Read the prompt and complete the frames. Strengthen your response with a convincing reason and relevant example. ▶

PROMPT: **Why is it important to provide detailed descriptions of characters in a story?**

When writing a story, it is important to provide detailed _____ of the

characters so that your readers can _____ their

_____ . In order to do this, you should include

plenty of _____ .

Construct a Response

Write
Discuss
Listen

Read the prompt and brainstorm ideas for a thoughtful response. Construct a response that includes a personal experience.

PROMPT: **Witnesses to a dispute or accident often provide a detailed description of the events. Think of a time when you witnessed an event. What details did you include in your description?**

_____

_____

_____

grammar tip ▶

Use **modal verbs**, or helping verbs, to give additional meaning to the main verb. Use *should* to make a suggestion or recommendation. Use *would* to show that something is possible under certain conditions. When you use a modal verb, add a verb in the base form.

EXAMPLE: I think you **should** enter the essay contest, but I **would** recommend checking the guidelines before submitting your essay.

clarify

clarify *verb*

DAY 1

The teacher used the vocabulary word in several _____ in

order to help _____ its meaning.

clarify *verb*

DAY 2

Several students didn't understand the _____ , so the

teacher _____ it for us.

DAY 3

The governor's recent speech was vague about his plans to _____

_____ , so the interviewer asked him to

_____ his statements.

DAY 4

The school has _____ its policy regarding

_____ in the new edition of the

student handbook.

DAY 5

After a classmate reviewed my essay, I decided to add more _____

to _____ my main argument.

TOTAL

SMARTSTART

DAY 1

REVIEW: clarify   *verb*

If you're speaking to someone who doesn't understand your language very

well, you can sometimes _____ your meaning by

_____ .

☐
☐

---

symbolize   *verb*

DAY 2

If I wanted to make a gift for my close friend to _____ our

friendship, I would make (a/an) _____ _____ .

☐
☐

DAY 3

The teacher explained that the _____

after the tumultuous, stormy night in the story was meant to

_____ relief and hope for the future.

☐
☐

DAY 4

I took an online quiz to find out which animal best _____ my

personality, and the result I received was (a/an) _____ _____ !

☐
☐

DAY 5

For many Americans, the _____ has come to

_____ the United States.

☐
☐

TOTAL

function

REVIEW: symbolize   *verb*

DAY 1

In my dreams, (a/an) _____ _____

usually _____ something I am worried or stressed about in

real life.

---

function   *noun*

DAY 2

The primary _____ of a library is to be a place where people

can _____ .

DAY 3

One of the most important _____ of a smartphone is the

ability to _____ .

DAY 4

A parent performs the _____ of many other jobs, such as

_____ and teacher.

DAY 5

Duct tape can perform many _____ around the house. For

example, you can use it to _____ .

TOTAL

18

SMARTSTART

REVIEW: function *noun*

DAY 1

One of the primary _____ of a hat is to

_____ .

☐
☐

---

feature *noun*

DAY 2

Tigers and house cats may be different, but one common _____

that both cats share is their _____ .

☐
☐

DAY 3

When shopping for a new car, consider which _____

is most important to you. For example, I prefer cars with a

_____ .

☐
☐

DAY 4

One of the key _____ that make my neighborhood unique is

its _____ .

☐
☐

DAY 5

In my opinion, one _____ all great movies have in common is

_____ .

☐
☐

TOTAL

coherent

REVIEW: feature *noun*

DAY 1

A prominent _____ of many national parks is (a/an) _____

_____ .

☐
☐

coherent *adjective*

DAY 2

When I first arrived in _____ for my study abroad

program, everyone spoke so quickly that the language barely seemed

_____ .

☐
☐

DAY 3

The founding members of our _____ worked together

to come up with (a/an) _____ _____ set of rules and

guidelines for our meetings.

☐
☐

DAY 4

You can make your writing more _____ by using

_____ .

☐
☐

DAY 5

My family didn't make a _____ plan for visiting the

_____ , so we didn't have enough time to see everything.

☐
☐

TOTAL

SMARTSTART

DAY 1

REVIEW: coherent   *adjective*

Even though I disagreed with his position, my opponent in the debate

made a _____ argument in favor of

_____ .

☐
☐

description   *noun*

DAY 2

Judging from my friend's lengthy _____ , it sounds like the

school dance on Friday was _____ !

☐
☐

DAY 3

Various witnesses to the _____ provided vastly different

_____ of what happened, so it was difficult for authorities

to piece together who was responsible.

☐
☐

DAY 4

I found one of my old journals while cleaning my room, and it was interesting to go

back and read my detailed _____ of (a/an) _____

_____ .

☐
☐

DAY 5

The author's _____ of the _____

_____ was so detailed, I could almost see it with my own eyes and feel

what it was like to be there.

☐
☐

TOTAL

Analyze Informational Text

Analyze means to carefully study.

Informational text can be found in many places, such as articles in a newspaper, magazine, textbook, or even on the Internet. **Informational text** provides important information about something and includes facts.

To **analyze informational text**, be sure to:
- read the title and headings
- read each section, paragraph, or list many times
- carefully study any pictures and charts
- discuss key ideas and important details
- think about what you've learned

 Find It   Read the sample texts below. Put a star next to the **informational text**.

Monkey Crosses the River

retold by John Manos

Crocodile watched Monkey hop from rock to rock to get across the river to eat from the large fruit tree. Crocodile had a plan to catch Monkey—he would pretend to be a rock!

Monkey was hopping across the river when he noticed that one rock was much larger than he remembered. Realizing immediately what was happening, he decided to outwit Crocodile once again.

"Hello, Rock!" Monkey cried out, but of course there was no answer.

America the Beautiful

by Dana Jensen and Dolores Johnson

In the 1800s, explorers traveling West came across landscapes that were unlike anything they'd seen before. They saw erupting geysers and gurgling hot springs. They trudged up tall, rocky mountains and stood under rushing waterfalls.

The explorers wanted to protect these places, so they set about convincing the United States Congress that the lands should be public, for everyone to enjoy.

Members of Congress viewed paintings and photos of these places. They read reports from people who had seen them in person. By 1872, they were convinced. Congress passed a bill creating Yellowstone National Park, the first of 58 national parks.

 Try It   **Analyze** the **informational text** by reading it several times. Then underline important details, and discuss what you learned using the sentence frames.

One fact I learned from the informational text is that Yellowstone National Park <u>has erupting geysers</u>

Another fact that I learned from the informational text is that <u>Congress passed a bill creating Yellowsto national park, the first of 58 national parks</u>

RATE WORD KNOWLEDGE

Circle the number that shows your knowledge of the words you'll use to analyze text.

6th Grade	7th Grade	RATE IT			
		BEFORE	8th Grade	AFTER	
analysis	introduce	1 2 3 (4)	**interpret**	1 2 3 4	
position	analyze	1 2 (3) 4	**critical**	1 2 3 4	
data	consider	1 2 3 (4)	**investigate**	1 2 3 4	
evidence	indicate	1 2 (3) 4	**factual**	1 2 3 4	
indicate	objective	1 (2) (3) 4	**present**	1 2 3 4	
concept	subjective	1 2 3 (4)	**summarize**	1 2 3 4	

DISCUSSION GUIDE
- Form groups of four.
- Assign letters to each person.
- Each group member takes a turn leading a discussion.
- Prepare to report about one word.

Ⓐ Ⓑ
Ⓓ Ⓒ

DISCUSS WORDS

Discuss how well you know the eighth grade words. Then, report to the class how you rated each word.

GROUP LEADER **Ask**

So, ___Nathan___ what do you know
(NAME)

about the word ___present___ ?

GROUP MEMBERS **Discuss**

1 = I **don't recognize** the word _____ .

I need to learn what it means.

2 = I **recognize** the word _____ ,

but I need to learn the meaning.

3 = I'm **familiar** with the word _____ .

I think it means _____ .

4 = I **know** the word _____ .

It's a _____ , and it means _____ .
(PART OF SPEECH)

Here is my example sentence: _____ .

REPORTER **Report Word Knowledge**

Our group gave the word _____ a rating of _____ because _____ .

SET A GOAL AND REFLECT

First, set a vocabulary goal for this unit by selecting at least three words that you plan to thoroughly learn. At the end of the unit, return to this page and write a reflection about one word you have mastered.

GOAL

During this unit I plan to thoroughly learn the words _____ ,

_____ , and _____ . Increasing my word knowledge will help

me speak and write effectively when I analyze informational _____ .

As a result of this unit, I feel most confident about the word _____ .

This is my model sentence: _____

_____ .

REFLECTION

interpret
verb

Say it:* in • **ter** • pret

 Write it: _interpret_   **Write it again:** _interpret_

 _____

Meaning
to decide on the meaning of
something

Examples
- When my little sister starts
  shouting it is easy to **interpret**
  that she is ___upset___ .

Synonyms
- explain, define, understand,
  make sense of

- After the final exams, our
  teacher **interpreted** the results
  and sent ___exceptional___
  reports to parents.

RATING
- ☑ Exceptional
- ☐ Exceeds requirements
- ☐ Meets requirements
- ☐ Needs improvement
- ☐ Poor

Forms
- **Present:**
  I/You/We/They interpret
  He/She/It interprets
- **Past:** interpreted

Family
- **Nouns:** interpretation, interpreter

Word Partners
- interpret the meaning of
- interpret the results

Examples
- It can be difficult to **interpret the meaning of** some modern art.
- Scientists have **interpreted the results** the new plant growth to
  mean that the forest fire did not cause as much damage as expected.

 Try It

I usually **interpret** someone's _____ to mean that he or she is

_____ .

VERBAL PRACTICE

Talk about it   Discuss ideas with your partner, listen to classmates, and then write your favorite idea.

Discuss
Listen
Write

1. I would feel nervous about being asked to **interpret** the meaning of (a/an) _____
   ___definition for a test when I didn't study___ .

2. It would be fantastic if our school **interpreted** the results of the student survey and

   offered a new class about ___biology___ .

interpret
verb

WRITING PRACTICE

Collaborate

Discuss
Agree
Write
Listen

Discuss ideas with your partner and agree on the best words to complete the frame. ▶

Many people have had disagreements because they have ___interpreted___ the tone

of (a/an) ___voice___ ___honking their horn___ incorrectly.

Our Turn

Discuss
Listen
Write

Read the prompt. Work with the teacher to complete the frames. Write a thoughtful response that includes a relevant example. ▶

PROMPT: Imagine that your science teacher has interpreted the results of a recent test to mean something negative. What will you do to prepare to retake the exam?

Our science teacher has ___interpreted___ our recent test scores to mean that

___we don't understand the unit___ . As a result,

I plan to ___study___ before

retaking the exam.

Be an Academic Author

Write
Discuss
Listen

Read the prompt and complete the frames. Strengthen your response with a personal experience.

PROMPT: Describe an exciting way you could interpret the meaning of your favorite movie to your classmates.

One way that I could ___interpret___ the meaning of my favorite movie,

___lilo & stitch___ , would be to create

(a/an) ___a___ ___scene___ . In particular, I would include details about how it

portrayed the importance of ___friendship and family___ .

Construct a Response

Write
Discuss
Listen

Read the prompt and brainstorm ideas for a thoughtful response. Construct a response that includes a personal experience.

PROMPT: Describe a time when a friend or family member interpreted your mood incorrectly and it caused a problem. Include your initial reaction and how you resolved the problem.

_____

_____

_____

grammar tip ▶

The **present perfect tense** is formed with *has/have* + past participle form of a verb. We use the present perfect tense to show that an action that took place in the past has an effect on the present. To write the past participle of a regular verb, add **-ed** or **-d** to the base form of the verb.

EXAMPLE: Since she **has received** her high school diploma she plans to attend college in the fall.

critical
adjective

 Write it: _____   **Write it again:** _____

 _____

TOOLKIT

Meaning	Examples
pointing out problems; very important	• My brother is very **critical** of my Halloween _____ because he doesn't like dressing up. 
Synonyms • disapproving	• It is **critical** that shoppers arrive at the store _____ or all of the new computers will be sold out. 

Family
- **Nouns:** criticism, critic
- **Verb:** criticize
- **Adverb:** critically

Word Partners
- highly critical
- of critical importance

Examples
- Carla is **highly critical** of the singers competing on television shows.
- In order to earn the total points, it is **of critical importance** to answer every question on the exam and avoid leaving any blanks.

 Try It

The movie reviewer was highly critical of the film's _____ .

VERBAL PRACTICE

Talk about it   Discuss ideas with your partner, listen to classmates, and then write your favorite idea.

Discuss
Listen
Write

1. Including a strong _____ is of **critical** importance in an essay.

2. The judges on the TV show _____ are highly **critical**.

WRITING PRACTICE

Collaborate

Discuss
Agree
Write
Listen

Discuss ideas with your partner and agree on the best words to complete the frame. ▶

Sometimes my _____ is highly _____ of my schoolwork because

(he/she) _____ wants me to _____ .

Our Turn

Discuss
Listen
Write

Read the prompt. Work with the teacher to complete the frames. Write a thoughtful response that includes a personal experience. ▶

PROMPT: **Describe a critical decision that a friend might make that you would strongly recommend thinking about carefully. What might happen if they don't?**

In my opinion, it is important to think carefully before making a _____

decision like _____ . Otherwise, you might

_____ .

Be an Academic Author

Write
Discuss
Listen

Read the prompt and complete the frames. Strengthen your response with a convincing reason. ▶

PROMPT: **Describe something that people do that you are usually highly critical about. Do you think your perspective is valid? Why?**

I am usually highly _____ when other people _____

_____ . I think my perspective (is/is not)

_____ valid because _____

_____ .

Construct a Response

Write
Discuss
Listen

Read the prompt and brainstorm ideas for a thoughtful response. Construct a response that includes relevant examples.

PROMPT: **Write about a time when someone made a critical remark or comment that hurt your feelings. How did you resolve the situation?**

My cousin said that I was stupid and that I don't know anything. I resolved the situation by not listening and thinking I can do anything, also to never give up.

grammar tip ▶

An **adverb** describes, or tells about, a verb. Adverbs usually end in *-ly*. Occasionally, adverbs come before the verb to describe how the action is done.

EXAMPLE: It is important to **carefully** review prior assignments before a test.

investigate
verb

 Write it: _investigate_   **Write it again:** _investigate_

 _____

Meaning	Examples
to try to find out information about something	• My father used a flashlight to **investigate** what was making noise around the garbage _cans_ . 
Synonyms	• Jane has fully **investigated** the language _class_ she is planning to take this summer.
• examine, research, explore	

TOOLKIT

Forms
- **Present:**
  I/You/We/They   investigate
  He/She/It   investigates
- **Past:**   investigated

Family
- **Nouns:** investigation, investigator
- **Adjective:** investigative

Word Partners
- fully/thoroughly investigate

- investigate the possibility of

Examples
- You should **thoroughly investigate** the plans and promises each candidate has made before voting for a new class president.
- Many shipping companies are making plans to **investigate the possibility of** self-driving delivery vehicles.

 Try It

When I heard news that ___there was a robbery at my friends house___

_____ , I had to **investigate** to find out if it was true.

VERBAL PRACTICE

Talk about it   Discuss ideas with your partner, listen to classmates, and then write your favorite idea.

**Discuss
Listen
Write**

1. Detectives **investigate** crimes by examining clues and ___the witnesses___

   _____ .

2. Scientists **investigate** natural disasters, such as _____ ,

   in order to learn how to predict when they might happen again.

WRITING PRACTICE

Collaborate

Discuss
Agree
Write
Listen

Discuss ideas with your partner and agree on the best words to complete the frame. ▶

Before registering for summer camp, you should fully _____investigate_____ the program to

see if activities like _____swimming_____ and _____cooking_____ are available.

Our Turn

Discuss
Listen
Write

Read the prompt. Work with the teacher to complete the frames. Write a thoughtful response that includes a convincing reason. ▶

PROMPT: Provide a thoughtful recommendation about classes that your school should investigate the possibility of offering next year. Why do you think students would enjoy them?

From my perspective, our school should _____investigate_____ the possibility of offering

_____ceramics_____ classes to students next year. The

reason I think students would enjoy such classes is that _____most____people_____

_____like to build and be creative_____ .

Be an Academic Author

Write
Discuss
Listen

Read the prompt and complete the frames. Strengthen your response with a personal experience.

PROMPT: Think about a topic or issue that you decided to fully investigate. What did you discover?

Once, when I was interested in _____swimming_____

_____ , I decided to _____investigate_____ it by _____watching the_____

_____Olympics_____ . Eventually, I discovered

that I'm able to _____compete in swimming_____ .

Construct a Response

Write
Discuss
Listen

Read the prompt and brainstorm ideas for a thoughtful response. Construct a response that includes relevant examples. ▶

PROMPT: Think about a career that you might like to have in the future. Describe two good ways to investigate the possibility of having that career and the steps you should take to reach it.

_____

_____

_____

grammar tip ▶

Use the **modal verb**, or helping verb, *should* to suggest or recommend something. When you use *should*, add a verb in the base form.

EXAMPLE: Parents **should** teach their children to look both ways before crossing the street.

factual
adjective

 Write it: Factual   **Write it again:** Factual

 _____   ~~GREAT~~

Meaning	Examples
based on information that is real or true	• Scientists __explain__ their theories with **factual** evidence rather than opinions.
Synonyms • true, real, accurate	• During the debate, the politicians gave __arguments__ that had a few **factual** errors.

Family
- **Noun:** fact
- **Adverb:** factually

Word Partners
- factual errors
- factual information

Examples
- Newspapers have a fact-checking team to avoid publishing articles that contain **factual errors.**
- My sister wanted to buy a new guitar, so she looked online to find **factual information** about the pros and cons of several popular brands.

 Try It

I recently searched the internet to find **factual** information about __starting a__
__buisness__ .

VERBAL PRACTICE

Talk about it

Discuss Listen Write

Discuss ideas with your partner, listen to classmates, and then write your favorite idea.

1. One **factual** statement about our school is that it has __3 science__

   __teachers__ .

2. After reading the directions to build (a/an) __a__ __lego set__ ,

   I discovered it contained several **factual** errors.

WRITING PRACTICE

Collaborate

Discuss
Agree
Write
Listen

Discuss ideas with your partner and agree on the best words to complete the frame. ▶

Many movies that include scenes with wild animals, such as ___The Jungle Book___

_____ , often have many ___factual___ errors.

Our Turn

Discuss
Listen
Write

Read the prompt. Work with the teacher to complete the frames. Write a thoughtful response that includes a convincing reason. ▶

PROMPT: Imagine that you are preparing to write a research report about an important historical figure. What would do to gather factual information about his or her life? Why is this important?

In preparing to write a research report about _____ ,

I would be sure to read _____ information about (his/her) _____ life in books

and online, while _____ . It is

important to include accurate information in order to _____

_____ .

Be an Academic Author

Write
Discuss
Listen

Read the prompt and complete the frames. Strengthen your response with a personal experience. ▶

PROMPT: Describe a time when you wanted to tell your best friend about something that happened to you in the past, but it was difficult to be completely factual. Why was it so difficult?

Once I wanted to tell my best friend about a time when I ___hit_____

_____ in elementary school. It was difficult to be

completely _____ because I _____

_____ .

Construct a Response

Write
Discuss
Listen

Read the prompt and brainstorm ideas for a thoughtful response. Construct a response that includes a personal experience. ▶

PROMPT: Most teachers provide feedback on written reports. Describe what you would do if the feedback you received pointed out several factual errors in your writing.

_____

_____

_____

grammar tip ▶

An **adjective** describes, or tells about, a noun. Usually an adjective goes before the noun it describes. An adjective sometimes appears after verbs such as *is, are, look, feel, smell,* and *taste.*

EXAMPLE: If you want to submit an **enticing** project for the art show, make sure to include **thoughtful** details in your artist's statement.

present
verb

Say it: pre • sent

Write it: present

Write it again: present

TOOLKIT

Meaning to give someone something; to share information	**Examples** • The coach **presented** his star players with _trophies_ for winning the World Series.
Synonyms • introduce; show; share	• Moving to a house with a big backyard **presented** an opportunity for us to adopt a _dog_.

Forms
- **Present:**
  - I/You/We/They   present
  - He/She/It   presents
- **Past:**   presented

Family
- **Noun:** presentation
- **Adjective:** presented

Word Partners
- present an opportunity

- present a challenge

Examples
- The museum's "Free Fridays" **present an opportunity** for everyone to see its beautiful collection of art.
- Budget cuts **present a challenge** to public schools.

 Try It

It always **presents** a challenge when my friends argue about _what to eat_ _____ .

VERBAL PRACTICE

Talk about it

Discuss ideas with your partner, listen to classmates, and then write your favorite idea.

Discuss
Listen
Write

1. The substitute teacher found that teaching the unruly students about the

_____ **presented** a challenge.

2. The student council is planning to **present** a program about

_____ .

WRITING PRACTICE

Collaborate
Discuss
Agree
Write
Listen

Discuss ideas with your partner and agree on the best words to complete the frame. ▶

The upcoming field trip ___presents___ an opportunity to learn more about

___or st___ .

Our Turn
Discuss
Listen
Write

Read the prompt. Work with the teacher to complete the frames. Write a thoughtful response that includes a convincing reason. ▶

PROMPT: **Describe how you present ideas in an essay. Why is this approach successful for you?**

When I write an essay, I ___present___ my ideas in a clear and

___meaningful___ manner. This approach has been successful for me because I am

usually able to ___make sure the idea is stated clearly and it is understandable___.

Be an Academic Author
Write
Discuss
Listen

Read the prompt and complete the frames. Strengthen your response with a relevant example. ▶

PROMPT: **Describe how extreme heat can present challenges to people in your community.**

Extreme heat can ___present___ challenges to people in my community. For

example, the heat could cause ___heat stroke___ , and

___children, elderly people, & homeless people___ would definitely need special

locations available for them to cool off and hydrate themselves.

Construct a Response
Write
Discuss
Listen

Read the prompt and brainstorm ideas for a thoughtful response. Construct a response that includes a relevant example. ▶

PROMPT: **Describe an issue that presents a challenge for you and your classmates, or a program that is offered at your school that presents an opportunity to learn something new.**

_____

_____

_____

grammar tip ▶

A **common noun** names a person, place, thing, or idea. **Singular nouns** name one person, place, thing, or idea. The words *a, an, one,* and *the* often appear before a singular noun.

EXAMPLE: The best story I know has **an** exciting setting, interesting characters, and **a** compelling plot.

summarize
verb

 Write it: _____ **Write it again:** _____

 _____

<table>
</table>

Meaning	Examples
to give only the most important information about something or someone	• Mr. Hood's chart **summarizes** important _____ about the Civil War. 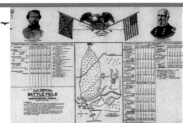
Synonyms • sum up	• At the beginning of each chapter, the _____ briefly **summarizes** the contents. 

TOOLKIT

Forms
- **Present:**
  I/You/We/They summarize
  He/She/It summarizes
- **Past:** summarized

Family
- **Noun:** summary

Word Partners
- briefly summarize
- summarize the results

Examples
- The reporter **briefly summarized** highlights from the previous day before presenting the latest news.
- For the science fair, we **summarized the results** of our study on a poster.

 Try It

Our teacher asked us to briefly **summarize** the main points of the _____.

VERBAL PRACTICE

Talk about it   Discuss ideas with your partner, listen to classmates, and then write your favorite idea.

Discuss
Listen
Write

1. My friend briefly **summarized** her experience at the new restaurant, but I had no idea that the ___Sashimi___ would be so delicious.

2. The substitute teacher **summarized** the results of her lesson about ___biology___ .

WRITING PRACTICE

Collaborate

Discuss
Agree
Write
Listen

Discuss ideas with your partner and agree on the best words to complete the frame. ▶

For homework, we had to briefly ___Summarize___ the results of our field trip to the ~~California Academy of Sciences (CAS)~~ .
Great America

Our Turn

Discuss
Listen
Write

Read the prompt. Work with the teacher to complete the frames. Write a thoughtful response that includes a convincing reason. ▶

PROMPT: Imagine that you are submitting an idea for an article that you would like to write to your school newspaper. How would you effectively summarize the issue so editors would select your idea?

One idea I would submit to the school newspaper would be about the issue of

___our watereolutions___ . I would effectively ___summarize___

this issue by _____ and

_____ .

Be an Academic Author

Write
Discuss
Listen

Read the prompt and complete the frames. Strengthen your response with a personal experience. ▶

PROMPT: Imagine that you have to present the results of a survey that you've conducted about your classmates' favorite after-school activities. Describe how you would visually summarize the results.

If I had to present the results of a survey about my classmates' favorite after-school activities,

I would visually ___summarize___ them with (a/an) ___bar___ ___graph___ .

The results would highlight how many classmates enjoy activities such as _____

_____ and _____ .

Construct a Response

Write
Discuss
Listen

Read the prompt and brainstorm ideas for a thoughtful response. Construct a response that includes convincing reasons.

PROMPT: Consider a time when you shared highlights about a favorite movie, game, book or activity with a friend. How did you summarize details about it so your friend would share your excitement?

Some time ago I summarized details about my favorite book, twilight.
I told them the book was good because of the difference in
people and how they get together.

---

grammar tip ▶

An **adverb** can describe, or tell about, a verb or an adjective. Adverbs usually end in **-ly** and come before the verb to describe its quality.

EXAMPLE: My cat seems **unusually** irritated and **oddly** nervous about new dog.

interpret

SMART *START*

REVIEW: description *noun*

DAY 1

I chose to write a _____ of my _____

_____ for the essay assignment about our

favorite place to visit.

☐

☐

---

interpret *verb*

DAY 2

I _____ my teacher's stern expression as a sign that she was

about to _____ .

☐

☐

DAY 3

We could _____ the results of our "favorite activity" poll to

mean that the students at our school like to _____ ,

since many students gave answers like soccer, swimming, biking, and basketball.

☐

☐

DAY 4

It was difficult to _____ the poem we read in English class,

because it was full of _____ .

☐

☐

DAY 5

When you know another person well, it can be easier to ___*interpret*___

the meaning of certain ___*expressions*___ .

☐

☐

TOTAL

SMART START

REVIEW: interpret *verb*

DAY 1

When viewing works of art, you can often _____ how the

artist was feeling based on the _____ .

☐

☐

---

critical *adjective*

DAY 2

Our teacher often states that it is _____ critical _____ that we always

_____ participate in class _____ , or else it will

count against our final grade.

☐

☐

DAY 3

When riding your bike on the street, it is of _____ importance

to always _____ .

☐

☐

DAY 4

My friend is highly _____ critical _____ of television shows and movies

that portray _____ in a negative light.

☐

☐

DAY 5

If you want to become a doctor or a nurse, it's _____ critical _____ that you

_____ stay positive _____ .

☐

☐

TOTAL

investigate

SMART START

REVIEW: critical   *adjective*

DAY 1

One figure who played a ____critical____ role in the founding of the United States is ____Benjamin Franklin____.

investigate   *verb*

DAY 2

I found an interesting summer program for young teens who want to ____learn self defense____, but my parents need to ____investigate____ it further before they will agree to spend money on it.

DAY 3

School administrators are fully _____ the recent reports of alleged _____ at our school.

DAY 4

If you want to make a difference in your community, you should ____investigate____ the possibilty of volunteering with an organization that ____serves food to the nomless____.

DAY 5

A news story my friend shared recently didn't seem ____accurate____ to me, so I ____investigated____ the claims it made and found that they were mostly exaggerated or false.

TOTAL

38

SMART START

REVIEW: investigate   *verb*

DAY 1

After several of our neighbors complained to the police about _____ *cyotes* _____ *roaming at night* _____ in the neighborhood, they sent a cruiser down to _____ *investigate* _____ .

factual   *adjective*

DAY 2

The characters and events in a work of fiction do not have to be _____ *factual* _____ , but they should be _____ *exciting* _____ or the reader will lose interest in the story.

DAY 3

Not all information you find online is _____ *factual* _____ . Many websites post items that are merely _____ .

DAY 4

There's a rumor that our town is building a new _____ *apartment complex* _____ in our neighborhood, but I'm not sure it's based on any _____ *factual* _____ evidence.

DAY 5

I know that my classmate's statement that she did not _____ *complete* _____ *her project* _____ is completely _____ *factual* _____ because I was an eyewitness.

TOTAL

39

present

REVIEW: factual   *adjective*

DAY 1

Though she delivered a stirring and persuasive speech, many of the statements

made by the _____ contained

_____ errors.

present   *verb*

DAY 2

The _____ I participated in last week

_____ me with quite a challenge, but I made it through

successfully.

DAY 3

A paper route or babysitting job can _____ middle school students with

an opportunity to _____ .

DAY 4

My classmates and I had a lot of fun when we _____ an entertaining play

about _____ at the school assembly.

DAY 5

A group of students and I wrote a letter to our principal and _____

our ideas for starting (a/an) _____ _____

_____ at our school.

TOTAL

SMART START

REVIEW: present *verb*

DAY 1

The construction of a new _____ in our town has

_____ local residents with an opportunity to have fun while

getting much-needed physical activity.

☐
☐

summarize *verb*

DAY 2

The news site _____ the results of the recent elections in

the form of a handy _____ .

☐
☐

DAY 3

A book review usually _____ the plot and conveys the

reviewer's _____ of the plot and writing style.

☐
☐

DAY 4

I recently found a greeting card for _____

_____ that perfectly _____ my feelings.

☐
☐

DAY 5

To very briefly _____ my favorite movie, I'd say that it's

about _____

_____ .

☐
☐

TOTAL

41

Cause and Effect

A **cause** makes something happen.
Ask yourself, "Why did it happen?"
To find the **cause**, look for clue words such as *since*, *because*, and *reason*.

An **effect** is what happens.
Ask yourself, "What happened?"
To find the **effect**, look for clue words such as *so*, *as a result*, and *therefore*.

 Find It   Read the sentences. Label the cause and the effect.

Our soccer team practiced hard. ➡ We won the match.

Our soccer team practiced hard **and as a result,** we won the match!
<u>_____</u>   <u>_____</u>
             Cause   Effect

My new cotton shirt shrank. ➡ I accidentally washed it in hot water.

My new cotton shirt shrank **because** I accidentally washed it in hot water.
<u>_____</u>   <u>_____</u>

_____   _____

 Try It   Complete the sentences. Then label the cause and the effect in each sentence.

I saved up money from babysitting **so** I was able to buy a _____.
<u>_____</u>   <u>_____</u>

_____   _____

I had to _____ on my library book **since** I returned it late to the library.
<u>_____</u>   <u>_____</u>

_____   _____

RATE WORD KNOWLEDGE

Circle the number that shows your knowledge of the words you'll use to speak and write about cause and effect.

6th Grade	7th Grade
influence	significance
reason	reaction
cause	various
factor	circumstance
lead	influence
impact	lead to

	RATE IT		
BEFORE	**8th Grade**	**AFTER**	
1 2 3 4	**alternative**	1 2 3 4	
1 2 3 4	**obstacle**	1 2 3 4	
1 2 3 4	**pattern**	1 2 3 4	
1 2 3 4	**potential**	1 2 3 4	
1 2 3 4	**trend**	1 2 3 4	
1 2 3 4	**resolution**	1 2 3 4	

DISCUSSION GUIDE
- Form groups of four.
- Assign letters to each person. Ⓐ Ⓑ
- Each group member takes a turn   Ⓓ Ⓒ
  leading a discussion.
- Prepare to report about one word.

DISCUSS WORDS

Discuss how well you know the eighth grade words. Then, report to the class how you rated each word.

GROUP LEADER | **Ask**

So, _____ what do you know
(NAME)

about the word _____ ?

GROUP MEMBERS | **Discuss**

1 = I **don't recognize** the word _____ .

I need to learn what it means.

2 = I **recognize** the word _____ ,

but I need to learn the meaning.

3 = I'm **familiar** with the word _____ .

I think it means _____ .

4 = I **know** the word _____ .

It's a _____ , and it means _____ .
(PART OF SPEECH)

Here is my example sentence: _____ .

REPORTER | **Report Word Knowledge**

Our group gave the word _____ a rating of _____ because _____ .

SET A GOAL AND REFLECT

First, set a vocabulary goal for this unit by selecting at least three words that you plan to thoroughly learn. At the end of the unit, return to this page and write a reflection about one word you have mastered.

GOAL

During this unit I plan to thoroughly learn the words _____ ,

_____ , and _____ . Increasing my word knowledge will

help me speak and write effectively about Cause and _____ .

As a result of this unit, I feel most confident about the word _____ .

This is my model sentence: _____

REFLECTION

_____ .

alternative

noun

Say it: al • **ter** • na • tive

Write it: _____   **Write it again:** _____

_____

TOOLKIT

Meaning a choice, solution, or plan of action that is different from another	**Examples** • My brother decided to ride his _____ to work as an **alternative** when his car wouldn't start. • When we ran out of _____ , my only **alternative** was to eat dry cereal.
Synonyms • choice; option	

Forms
- **Singular:** alternative
- **Plural:** alternatives

Family
- **Verb:** alternate
- **Adjectives:** alternate; alternative
- **Adverb:** alternatively

Word Partners
- offer an alternative

- only/best alternative

Examples
- If you don't want mashed potatoes, ask the waiter to **offer an alternative** for your meal.
- My nephew is allergic to wheat, so my **only alternative** was to make him a gluten-free pizza with a cornmeal crust.

 Try It

During the holidays, I didn't want to eat _____ , so my grandmother offered green beans as an **alternative**.

VERBAL PRACTICE

Talk about it

Discuss Listen Write

Discuss ideas with your partner, listen to classmates, and then write your favorite idea.

1. When it comes to choosing (a/an) _____ _____ , students at our school have numerous **alternatives**.

2. My brother is willing to eat _____ when it is the only **alternative**.

alternative

noun

WRITING PRACTICE

Collaborate

Discuss
Agree
Write
Listen

Discuss ideas with your partner and agree on the best words to complete the frame. ▶

There are many _____ for people who don't eat fish, such as _____

_____ and _____ .

Our Turn

Discuss
Listen
Write

Read the prompt. Work with the teacher to complete the frames. Write a thoughtful response that includes a personal experience.

PROMPT: **Describe a situation when a family member was doing something that made it difficult for you to study. What did you do as an alternative?**

Once, my _____ was _____

_____ , which made it nearly impossible for me to study for

(a/an) _____ _____ . So my only

_____ was to _____ .

Be an Academic Author

Write
Discuss
Listen

Read the prompt and complete the frames. Strengthen your response with a convincing reason. ▶

PROMPT: **Imagine that you have an opportunity to offer alternatives for your school cafeteria's menu. Why would students appreciate the new choices?**

If I had the opportunity to offer _____ for our school cafeteria's menu, I would

suggest _____ instead of hot dogs.

Several students, particularly our _____ classmates, would

appreciate the new choice because they _____ .

Construct a Response

Write
Discuss
Listen

Read the prompt and brainstorm ideas for a thoughtful response. Construct a response that includes relevant examples and a convincing reason. ▶

PROMPT: **Not everyone can attend college right after high school. What are some alternatives that might help a high school graduate gain knowledge and skills to start college later?**

_____

_____

_____

grammar tip ▶

Quantity adjectives tell "how much" or "how many." Quantity adjectives go before a plural noun. Common quantity adjectives are: *most, many, some, several, both, numerous.*

EXAMPLE: In New York city, there are **numerous alternatives** to driving. For example, my grandfather always carries **several coins** in his jacket pocket for the subway.

alternative **45**

obstacle

noun

 Write it: _____   **Write it again:** _____

 _____

TOOLKIT

Meaning something that makes it difficult for a person to succeed	**Examples** • The rider and her horse easily _____ over all the **obstacles** on the course. 
Synonyms • problem	• After losing his eyesight, one **obstacle** my cousin had to overcome was learning how to read _____ . 

Forms
- **Singular:** obstacle
- **Plural:** obstacles

Word Partners
- a major obstacle

- overcome an/some/many obstacle(s)

Examples
- The loud children in the theater were **a major obstacle** to our enjoyment of the movie.
- My parents grew up in poor neighborhoods, and they had to **overcome many obstacles** to obtain their college degrees.

 Try It

I thought our limited _____ would be a major **obstacle** during our trip to Peru, but we were resourceful and managed to enjoy the experience.

VERBAL PRACTICE

Talk about it   Discuss ideas with your partner, listen to classmates, and then write your favorite idea.

> Discuss
> Listen
> Write

1. One major **obstacle** to finishing my book report on time was that I _____ _____ .

2. When I _____ for the first time I had to overcome the **obstacle** of my own fear.

WRITING PRACTICE

Collaborate

Discuss
Agree
Write
Listen

Discuss ideas with your partner and agree on the best words to complete the frame. ▶

When conducting an experiment in science class, _____

_____ might be a major _____ to ensuring lab safety.

Our Turn

Discuss
Listen
Write

Read the prompt. Work with the teacher to complete the frames. Write a thoughtful response that includes a personal experience. ▶

PROMPT: **Planning a successful event can be filled with obstacles. Think of an event you would like to help plan. What obstacles might you face before the event?**

I would like to help plan (a/an) _____ _____ .

One _____ I might face before the event is _____

_____ . Another is that I wouldn't know

whether the people we invited would _____ .

Be an Academic Author

Write
Discuss
Listen

Read the prompt and complete the frames. Strengthen your response with a relevant example. ▶

PROMPT: **If you were going camping with your family, what would be a major obstacle to having an enjoyable trip? How might you overcome this obstacle?**

If I were camping with my family, one major _____ to having an enjoyable trip

would be if _____ .

We might overcome it by preparing ahead of time and making sure we _____

_____ .

Construct a Response

Write
Discuss
Listen

Read the prompt and brainstorm ideas for a thoughtful response. Construct a response that includes a personal experience.

PROMPT: **Every school year brings new obstacles for students. Think of an obstacle you faced last year in a class or an extracurricular activity. How did you overcome it?**

_____

_____

_____

grammar tip ▶

Use the **modal verb**, or helping verb, *might* to show that something is possible. When you use *might*, add a verb in the base form.

EXAMPLE: We **might go** for a run this afternoon, but it **might be** too hot.

pattern

noun

 Write it: _____ **Write it again:** _____

 _____

Meaning	**Examples**	
a repeated set of events, characteristics, or features	• On New Year's Day, many people decide to _____ the **pattern** of an unhealthy behavior.	
	• When Martha empties the _____ , she follows a **pattern** that begins with putting away cups and ends with storing the utensils.	

Forms
- **Singular:** pattern
- **Plural:** patterns

Family
- **Verb:** pattern
- **Adjective:** patterned

Word Partners
- follow a pattern

- pattern of behavior

Examples
- During a physical exam, the doctor **follows a pattern** to check her patient's height, weight, blood pressure, and overall health.
- The police detective discovered a **pattern of behavior**, which led to the successful capture of the thief.

 Try It

On Saturdays, my **pattern** of behavior usually includes _____ .

 VERBAL PRACTICE

Talk about it   Discuss ideas with your partner, listen to classmates, and then write your favorite idea.

Discuss
Listen
Write

1. Teachers look for **patterns** of errors when reviewing _____

   _____ to identify content that needs to be retaught.

2. During our group project, we had to follow a **pattern** in order to _____

   _____ .

WRITING PRACTICE

Collaborate

Discuss
Agree
Write
Listen

Discuss ideas with your partner and agree on the best words to complete the frame. ▶

Many Internet apps track online search _____ in order to target ads that match a

person's _____ .

Our Turn

Discuss
Listen
Write

Read the prompt. Work with the teacher to complete the frames. Write a thoughtful response that includes a convincing reason.

PROMPT: **Describe the pattern that you typically follow in the morning before school. Why do you do things in this order?**

Typically, I follow a _____ each morning before school. First, I usually

_____ and then I _____

_____ . I complete these tasks in this order because I

_____ .

Be an Academic Author

Write
Discuss
Listen

Read the prompt and complete the frames. Strengthen your response with a relevant example. ▶

PROMPT: **Imagine that you noticed an unusual pattern of behavior from a special person or a cherished pet. What would you be sure to do?**

If I noticed that my _____ had an unusual _____ of

behavior, I would definitely want to help (him/her) _____ . For example, if (he/she)

_____ began to _____ I would be

sure to _____ .

Construct a Response

Write
Discuss
Listen

Read the prompt and brainstorm ideas for a thoughtful response. Construct a response that includes relevant examples. ▶

PROMPT: **Identify a particular skill, such as playing an instrument or learning a language, that you would like to accomplish in the future. Describe the pattern that you would follow to master this skill.**

_____

_____

_____

grammar tip ▶

The **preposition to** needs to be followed by a verb in the base form.

EXAMPLE: Most veterans say that citizens need **to study** history in order to avoid making the same mistakes in the future.

potential
adjective

 Write it: _____   **Write it again:** _____

_____

TOOLKIT

Meaning
having the ability to become a kind of person or thing

Synonyms
• possible; likely

Examples
• Their song _____ were so fantastic that everyone thought they were the **potential** winners.

• During the summer, high _____ are a **potential** risk to athletes.

Family
• **Noun:** potential
• **Adverb:** potentially

Word Partners
• potential benefits/problems

• potential risk(s)

Examples
• Research suggests there may be **potential benefits** to drinking more water.
• Scientists are studying the **potential risks** of a new mosquito-borne virus.

 Try It
Not getting enough _____ can be a **potential** problem for teens.

VERBAL PRACTICE

Talk about it

    Discuss
    Listen
    Write

Discuss ideas with your partner, listen to classmates, and then write your favorite idea.

1. One **potential** risk when riding a bike is that you might _____ .

2. If all students were required to use e-books instead of print textbooks, _____ _____ could be a **potential** problem.

WRITING PRACTICE

Collaborate

Discuss
Agree
Write
Listen

Discuss ideas with your partner and agree on the best words to complete the frame. ▶

Our class is full of _____ doctors and _____ who just

need to _____ in order to achieve their goals.

Our Turn

Discuss
Listen
Write

Read the prompt. Work with the teacher to complete the frame. Write a thoughtful response that includes a relevant example. ▶

PROMPT: **What are two potential benefits to learning another language.**

Two _____ benefits to learning another language are _____

_____ and being able to

_____ . For example, if I learned to

speak _____ , I would be able to visit _____

and make new friends or have an interesting career.

Be an Academic Author

Write
Discuss
Listen

Read the prompt and complete the frames. Strengthen your response with a relevant example. ▶

PROMPT: **Describe one thing you do almost every day that involves a potential risk. What do you do to minimize the potential harm from the risk?**

One thing I do frequently that involves a _____ risk is _____

_____ . To minimize the _____

harm, I make sure to _____

every time.

Construct a Response

Write
Discuss
Listen

Read the prompt and brainstorm ideas for a thoughtful response. Construct a response that includes relevant examples. ▶

PROMPT: **Describe what you perceive to be the potential risks of self-driving cars. What ideas do you have to prevent some of the risks?**

_____

_____

_____

grammar tip ▶

Count nouns name things that can be counted. Count nouns have two forms, singular and plural. To make most count nouns plural, add -s. To make count nouns that end in *x, ch, sh, ss,* and *z,* plural, add -es.

EXAMPLE: Dr. Hancock teaches music **classes** at the community center. I help her organize the **instruments**.

trend

noun

Say it: trend

 Write it: _____   **Write it again:** _____

 _____

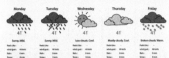

TOOLKIT

Meaning
a general direction or movement toward something

Examples
- The weather report showed a **trend** of _____ ahead.

- The magazine article described a **trend** toward wearing patches on _____ jackets.

Synonyms
- course; inclination

Forms
- **Singular:** trend
- **Plural:** trends

Family
- **Verb:** trend
- **Adjective:** trendy

Word Partners
- trend toward

- reverse the trend

Examples
- Recently, there is a **trend toward** sending holiday cards with funny family photos.
- By removing the soda machines from the cafeteria, our principal is hoping to **reverse the trend** of students drinking sugary drinks.

 Try It

Among teenagers there is a **trend** toward _____ .

VERBAL PRACTICE

Talk about it   Discuss ideas with your partner, listen to classmates, and then write your favorite idea.

Discuss
Listen   1. Some politicians argue that we need to reverse the **trend** of _____
Write
_____ .

2. From my perspective, _____ is a new **trend** on

digital devices.

trend

noun

WRITING PRACTICE

Collaborate

Discuss
Agree
Write
Listen

Discuss ideas with your partner and agree on the best words to complete the frame. ▶

During the class discussion, students agreed that we needed to do something to reverse

the _____ of _____ at our school.

Our Turn

Discuss
Listen
Write

Read the prompt. Work with the teacher to complete the frames. Write a thoughtful response that includes a convincing reason. ▶

PROMPT: **Describe a recent trend you've noticed in movies, books, or TV shows that teens seem to prefer. Why do you think it is so popular?.**

Recently, I've noticed a _____ in (movies, books, TV shows)

_____ about _____ .

One reason they might be popular is that teens like to _____

_____ .

Be an Academic Author

Write
Discuss
Listen

Read the prompt and complete the frames. Strengthen your response with a personal experience. ▶

PROMPT: **Think about an article of clothing that was popular when you were younger. What happened that reversed this trend?**

In elementary school, wearing _____

was popular among _____ .

However, when _____

_____ , it completely reversed this _____ .

Construct a Response

Write
Discuss
Listen

Read the prompt and brainstorm ideas for a thoughtful response. Construct a response that includes a personal experience. ▶

PROMPT: **Negative news in magazines, online, or on television can significantly impact a product's popularity. Describe how news about a particular product reversed the trend in its popularity.**

_____

_____

_____

grammar tip ▶

A **past-tense verb** describes an action that already happened. For verbs that end in silent *e*, drop the final *e* before you add *-ed*.

EXAMPLE: Yesterday, we **decided** to go to the mall. My sister **realized** that she **liked** eating pretzels

resolution

noun

Say it: res • o • **lu** • tion

 Write it: _____   **Write it again:** _____

 _____

TOOLKIT

Meaning a promise to do something; the solution to a problem or difficulty	**Examples** • The sisters couldn't _____ on what to watch, so the only **resolution** was for their dad to decide on a show.

Synonyms • solution	• After failing a class in college, my cousin made a **resolution** to study _____ frequently.

Forms
- **Singular:** resolution
- **Plural:** resolutions

Family
- **Verb:** resolve
- **Adjectives:** resolute, resolved
- **Adverb:** resolutely

Word Partners
- resolution(s) to

- peaceful/productive/ successful resolution(s)

Examples
- After gaining twenty pounds, my aunt made two **resolutions to** eat fewer sugary snacks and exercise daily.
- After several parents complained, we were all relieved to hear about the **peaceful resolution** to the parking problem at the high school campus

 Try It

I think all teens my age should make a **resolution** to _____

_____ .

VERBAL PRACTICE

Talk about it

> Discuss
> Listen
> Write

Discuss ideas with your partner, listen to classmates, and then write your favorite idea.

1. Community members are hopeful that the recent _____

_____ near the hospital will end with a peaceful **resolution**.

2. Our _____ teacher asked us to find a productive **resolution**

to the recent trend of students arriving late to his class.

WRITING PRACTICE

Collaborate

Discuss
Agree
Write
Listen

Discuss ideas with your partner and agree on the best words to complete the frame. ▶

It is often difficult to find successful _____ to complex problems such as

_____ and _____ .

Our Turn

Discuss
Listen
Write

Read the prompt. Work with the teacher to complete the frames. Write a thoughtful response that includes a personal experience.

PROMPT: **Think about an incident when a particular type of communication, such as a note, text, or email, led to a misunderstanding. What led to a successful resolution to the misunderstanding?**

Once, I (sent/received) _____ (a/an) _____ _____

that _____ a misunderstanding. As a result, I made sure

to _____ , which led to a

successful _____ .

Be an Academic Author

Write
Discuss
Listen

Read the prompt and complete the frames. Strengthen your response with a personal experience.

PROMPT: **Describe an argument that you had with a best friend. What was the resolution?**

Once, my best friend and I had an argument about _____

_____ . Fortunately, we came to a peaceful _____

by _____ .

Construct a Response

Write
Discuss
Listen

Read the prompt and brainstorm ideas for a thoughtful response. Construct a response that includes a personal experience. ▶

PROMPT: **Group projects can provide opportunities for classmates to share creative ideas and reach a resolution to an assigned problem. Describe a time when working as a team prevented you from completing an assignment successfully.**

_____

_____

_____

grammar tip ▶

The **preposition** to needs to be followed by a verb in the base form.

EXAMPLE: Many high school students are ready **to choose** what they plan to study when they go to college.

alternative

REVIEW: summarize *verb*

DAY 1

I had to miss the _____ yesterday, but my friend

_____ the important highlights.

---

alternative *noun*

DAY 2

I really don't want to _____ this afternoon, but I don't

see another _____ , since it's my responsibility and it's

expected of me.

DAY 3

Our school offers some elective courses for students, such as _____

_____ , but there are other schools with larger budgets

that can offer even more _____ .

DAY 4

My father didn't like the fit of the _____ he tried on, so

the salesperson brought him some other _____ to choose

from.

DAY 5

The cafeteria is serving _____ today, which I don't

like very much. I wish there were a better _____ !

TOTAL

 **SMART**START

obstacle

DAY 1

REVIEW: alternative   *noun*

If someone has knee problems and is looking for a good _____ to running, I might suggest _____ as a source of exercise.

---

obstacle   *noun*

DAY 2

A major _____ to my hopes for getting a puppy is my mother's concern that _____ .

DAY 3

One of the many _____ that new immigrants must overcome is learning the _____ of their new country.

DAY 4

One _____ I might face when I begin high school is _____ _____ .

DAY 5

There are several _____ to becoming a great musician. It requires a great deal of _____ .

TOTAL

pattern

REVIEW: obstacle   *noun*

DAY 1

One of the _____ my parents faced when buying a house

was that many properties on the market were too _____ .

☐
☐

---

pattern   *noun*

DAY 2

Many mystery stories follow a similar _____ , which

makes them a bit _____ . It's refreshing when a story does

something unexpected!

☐
☐

DAY 3

Family vacations often follow a similar _____ : at first,

everyone is excited, but by the end, everyone is _____ .

☐
☐

DAY 4

Our cousins' dog was developing some _____ of

_____ behavior, so they had to hire a trainer to work

with him.

☐
☐

DAY 5

Although many people stick to a daily routine, some prefer not to follow a set

_____ , preferring instead to seek _____ in

their everyday lives.

☐
☐

TOTAL

SMART START

REVIEW: pattern *noun*

DAY 1

I'd like to change some of my negative _____ of behavior, such as my tendency to _____ .

potential *adjective*

DAY 2

One of the _____ benefits of taking a walk every day is that it can help you _____ .

DAY 3

One of the _____ risks of _____ is that you could seriously injure yourself.

DAY 4

_____ is one of our _____ destinations for our family vacation.

DAY 5

Given my skills and interests, one of the _____ careers I may pursue is that of (a/an) _____ _____ .

TOTAL

trend

SMARTSTART

REVIEW: potential   *adjective*

DAY 1

One _____ problem we could face while hiking in the woods is

(a/an) _____ _____ .

---

trend   *noun*

DAY 2

I think our society treats _____ unfairly, which

is a _____ we should reverse.

DAY 3

In online discourse, there has been an unfortunate _____

toward _____ comments, especially between strangers

who disagree about an issue.

DAY 4

There is a current _____ among students at my school to

wear _____ .

DAY 5

As climate change progresses, we're seeing a _____ toward

_____ .

TOTAL

REVIEW: **trend**   *noun*

DAY 1

One positive _____ we're seeing now is an increase in middle school

students who are willing to _____ .

☐

☐

---

resolution   *noun*

DAY 2

When you have a disagreement with a loved one, even when you feel that he or she is

behaving _____ , it's important to try to reach a peaceful

_____ .

☐

☐

DAY 3

Recently, I was having a problem getting our _____ to work,

but it turned out that the _____ to the problem was simply

to turn it off and turn it back on again.

☐

☐

DAY 4

Many people in this country disagree strongly on the issue of

_____ , and I'm not sure we will ever come

to a _____ on it.

☐

☐

DAY 5

When we couldn't agree on what to have for lunch, my friend and I decided that the

_____ would be to _____

_____ .

☐

☐

TOTAL

Toolkit Unit 4 | Sequence

Sequence

Sequence is the order in which events happen.

Use the signal words *first*, *next* and *last*, along with the Toolkit words in this unit to help you analyze, discuss, and write about the **sequence** of events.

Find It Read the sentences. Determine the sequence and write **1st**, **2nd**, and **3rd** to show the order in which the events happen.

1. _____ I bought her a new book and gave it to her on her birthday. She loved it.

   _____ The next day, I saw her reading the very same book!

   _____ Last week, I bought my sister a book for her birthday.

2. _____ Afterwards, we still had some apples left over, so we gave some to our neighbor.

   _____ When we got home, we used most of the apples to make two apple pies.

   _____ On Saturday, my family went apple picking at an orchard.

Try It Show the **sequence** by describing something that might occur after the first and second events.

1. Before you start writing an essay, you need to research the topic carefully.

2. As you write the essay, you should be sure to _____
   _____ .

3. Lastly, before you hand your essay in, you need to check it to _____
   _____ .

RATE WORD KNOWLEDGE

Circle the number that shows your knowledge of the words you'll use to speak and write about sequence.

6th Grade	7th Grade	BEFORE	8th Grade	AFTER
		RATE IT		
after	requirement	1 2 3 4	current	1 2 3 4
beforehand	priority	1 2 3 4	phase	1 2 3 4
subsequently	initial	1 2 3 4	transition	1 2 3 4
eventually	series	1 2 3 4	consequently	1 2 3 4
currently	prior	1 2 3 4	eventually	1 2 3 4
precede	process	1 2 3 4	ultimate	1 2 3 4

DISCUSSION GUIDE
- Form groups of four.
- Assign letters to each person.
- Each group member takes a turn leading a discussion.
- Prepare to report about one word.

DISCUSS WORDS

Discuss how well you know the eighth grade words. Then, report to the class how you rated each word.

GROUP LEADER **Ask**

So, _____ what do you know
          (NAME)

about the word _____ ?

GROUP MEMBERS **Discuss**

1 = I **don't recognize** the word _____ .

I need to learn what it means.

2 = I **recognize** the word _____ ,

but I need to learn the meaning.

3 = I'm **familiar** with the word _____ .

I think it means _____ .

4 = I **know** the word _____ .

It's a _____ , and it means _____ .
        (PART OF SPEECH)

Here is my example sentence: _____ .

REPORTER **Report Word Knowledge**

Our group gave the word _____ a rating of _____ because _____ .

SET A GOAL AND REFLECT

First, set a vocabulary goal for this unit by selecting at least three words that you plan to thoroughly learn. At the end of the unit, return to this page and write a reflection about one word you have mastered.

GOAL

During this unit I plan to thoroughly learn the words _____ ,

_____ , and _____ . Increasing my word knowledge will

help me speak and write effectively about _____ .

As a result of this unit, I feel most confident about the word _____ .

This is my model sentence: _____

_____ .

REFLECTION

current

adjective

Say it: cur • rent

 Write it: _____ **Write it again:** _____

 _____

Meaning	Examples
belonging to the present time	• The **current** issue of _____ magazine has cupcakes on the cover.

Synonyms	
• present	• My grandparents seem to really enjoy the **current** trend of _____ at their gym.

Family
• **Adverb:** currently

Word Partners
• current events
• current trend

Examples
• Many people read the newspaper to find out about **current events**.
• A **current trend** among many elementary school soccer players is to wear different colored socks.

 Try It

During winter it is difficult to find **current** events involving certain Olympic sports, such as

_____ .

VERBAL PRACTICE

Talk about it

Discuss
Listen
Write

Discuss ideas with your partner, listen to classmates, and then write your favorite idea.

1. I usually hear about **current** events from _____ .

2. My **current** _____ teacher is fantastic.

current
adjective

WRITING PRACTICE

Collaborate
Discuss
Agree
Write
Listen

Discuss ideas with your partner and agree on the best words to complete the frame. ▶

One _____ fashion trend is to wear _____

with _____ .

Our Turn
Discuss
Listen
Write

Read the prompt. Work with the teacher to complete the frames. Write a thoughtful response that includes a convincing reason. ▶

PROMPT: **Describe a current event that recently caught your attention. Why did the commentary or piece resonate with you?**

Recently, a _____ event that caught my attention was a commentary about

_____ . This piece resonates with me

because I am particularly concerned about _____ .

Be an Academic Author
Write
Discuss
Listen

Read the prompt and complete the frames. Strengthen your response with relevant examples.

PROMPT: **What is one of your current interests? How does this interest compare to what you were interested in when you were five years old?** ▶

One of my _____ interests is _____

_____ . However, when I was five, I was more interested in _____

_____ .

Construct a Response
Write
Discuss
Listen

Read the prompt and brainstorm ideas for a thoughtful response. Construct a response that includes a relevant example and a convincing reason. ▶

PROMPT: **Describe a current trend in music or sports that many of your friends appreciate, but that you do not enjoy. Why is your perspective or opinion different from that of your friends?**

_____

_____

_____

grammar tip ▶
An **adjective** describes, or tells about, a noun. Usually an adjective goes before the noun it describes.

EXAMPLE: The **devoted** fans braved **miserable** weather to cheer on their team at the **first** game of the season.

current **65**

phase
noun

Say it: phase

 Write it: _____ **Write it again:** _____

 _____

Meaning a stage or step in a process, or a period of time in which someone or something changes or develops	**Examples** • An _____ crocodile is terrifying, but in its first **phases** of development it is rather adorable.
Synonyms • stage; step	• The city of Flint has been going through a _____ **phase** due to the water crisis.

Forms
- **Singular:** phase
- **Plural:** phases

Family
- **Verb:** phase

Word Partners
- enter a new phase
- final phase

Examples
- Relations between the two countries **entered a new phase** after the appointment of a thoughtful new ambassador.
- Construction on the new library is in its **final phase** and students are looking forward to reading the new books.

 Try It

Now that all of the permission slips have been turned in, plans for our upcoming field trip to the _____ are in the final **phase**.

VERBAL PRACTICE

Talk about it   Discuss ideas with your partner, listen to classmates, and then write your favorite idea.

Discuss
Listen
Write

1. The final **phase** of my _____ assignment includes proofreading.

2. Most young children enter a new **phase** of life when they learn how to

_____ .

phase

noun

WRITING PRACTICE

Collaborate

Discuss
Agree
Write
Listen

Discuss ideas with your partner and agree on the best words to complete the frame. ▶

Building (a/an) _____ _____ does not

happen overnight; it involves several _____ .

Our Turn

Discuss
Listen
Write

Read the prompt. Work with the teacher to complete the frames. Write a thoughtful response that includes a convincing reason.

PROMPT: **Think about some of the different phases of life that possible in the future. Describe one phase that you look forward to entering in the years ahead? Why?**

In the future, I look forward to entering a _____ of life that involves

_____ . The reason this phase

is appealing is because I _____ .

Be an Academic Author

Write
Discuss
Listen

Read the prompt and complete the frames. Strengthen your response with relevant examples.

PROMPT: **Imagine that you have to write a report about a wild animal's life. What creature would you be most interested in writing about? What are some of the phases it experiences?** ▶

If I had to write a report about a wild animal, I would be most interested in writing about

(a/an) _____ _____ . This animal's life has

several _____ , including a time when it _____

_____ . This creature also experiences a change when it

_____ .

Construct a Response

Write
Discuss
Listen

Read the prompt and brainstorm ideas for a thoughtful response. Construct a response that includes personal experiences. ▶

PROMPT: **Describe some of the phases involved in buying something from a store.**

_____

_____

_____

grammar tip ▶

Quantity adjectives tell "how much" or "how many." Quantity adjectives go before a plural noun. Common quantity adjectives are: *most, many, some, several, both, numerous.*

EXAMPLE: A frog's life has **several** stages. There are **many** ways to reach my house. There are **numerous** mistakes in your paper.

transition
noun

Say it: tran • **si** • tion

 Write it: _____   **Write it again:** _____

 _____

<table>
<tr><td rowspan="2">TOOLKIT</td></tr>
</table>

Meaning a change from one thing to another	**Examples** • The crazy kitten finally went through a **transition** and became a calm _____ cat.
Synonyms change; shift; switch	• Most students walk quickly during the **transition** between _____ so they aren't late.

Forms
- **Singular:** transition
- **Plural:** transitions

Family
- **Verb:** transition
- **Adjective:** transitional

Word Partners
- period of transition
- smooth/difficult transition

Examples
- There is a brief **period of transition** between the outgoing and the newly elected presidents.
- For the two children in the Kwan family, moving from Shanghai to Chicago was a **difficult transition**.

 Try It

Using words and phrases like *at first*, and _____ in your writing can help you make smooth **transitions** from one point to another.

VERBAL PRACTICE

Talk about it

Discuss
Listen
Write

Discuss ideas with your partner, listen to classmates, and then write your favorite idea.

1. In northern states, the **transition** from summer to winter usually means we get to

_____ .

2. If you're making a **transition** from a big house to a small apartment, you will need to get

rid of any extra _____ .

transition
noup

noun

WRITING PRACTICE

Collaborate

Discuss
Agree
Write
Listen

Discuss ideas with your partner and agree on the best words to complete the frame. ▶

Many high schools work hard to help students make a smooth _____ from

middle school by _____ .

Our Turn

Discuss
Listen
Write

Read the prompt. Work with the teacher to complete the frames. Write a thoughtful response that includes a personal experience. ▶
PROMPT: Think about a time when you went through a transition in your life. Was it smooth or difficult? As you reflect on the experience, what did you learn about yourself?

Once, I went through a (difficult/smooth) _____ _____ in my

life when I _____ . As I

reflect on the experience, I learned that I am capable of _____

_____ .

Be an Academic Author

Write
Discuss
Listen

Read the prompt and complete the frames. Strengthen your response with a convincing reason. ▶
PROMPT: What would you suggest to help someone remember and analyze a dream after the hazy period of transition between sleep and wakefulness? How can analyzing a dream be helpful?

It's easy to forget a dream during the hazy period of _____ between sleep and

wakefulness. However, if you keep a _____ next to your bed, you

can record everything you remember right away. When you analyze a dream, it helps you to

_____ .

Construct a Response

Write
Discuss
Listen

Read the prompt and brainstorm ideas for a thoughtful response. Include a convincing reason to strengthen your response. ▶
PROMPT: Imagine that you have just received a new pet. What are some transitions that the animal and your family members might experience as everyone adjusts to the new pet?

_____

_____

_____

grammar tip ▶

Adjectives are always singular even if they describe a plural noun. Do not add **-s** to adjectives that describe plural nouns.

EXAMPLE: Strong paragraphs include **important** details about several **interesting** facts.

transition **69**

consequently
adverb

 Write it: _____   **Write it again:** _____

 _____

TOOLKIT

Meaning **as a result**	**Examples** • Someone was texting while driving and **consequently** _____ into the back of my sister's car.
Synonyms • thus; therefore	• A little girl began _____ in the restaurant. **Consequently,** her mother had to take her outside.

Family
- **Noun:** consequence
- **Adjective:** consequent

Word Partners
- Consequently,

- and consequently

Examples
- A bully pushed another student against a locker yesterday. **Consequently**, he was suspended.
- The ladder I used to reach the book on the top shelf was old and wobbly, **and consequently** I tumbled to the floor.

 Try It

I've been feeling really tired and lazy lately. **Consequently,** I've decided I need to _____
_____ .

VERBAL PRACTICE

Talk about it   Discuss ideas with your partner, listen to classmates, and then write your favorite idea.

Discuss
Listen
Write

1. My sister added too much _____ to the stew she was making, and **consequently**, it had to be thrown out.

2. I greatly improved my English essay by _____
_____ . **Consequently,** I received a satisfactory final grade.

consequently
adverb

WRITING PRACTICE

Collaborate

Discuss
Agree
Write
Listen

Discuss ideas with your partner and agree on the best words to complete the frame. ▶

My family wanted to try the new _____ restaurant in town, but it was

too _____ . _____ , we decided to go somewhere else.

Our Turn

Discuss
Listen
Write

Read the prompt. Work with the teacher to complete the frames. Write a thoughtful response that includes a personal experience. ▶
PROMPT: Think of a time when a close friend did something hurtful that consequently affected your friendship. How did you react to the situation? What happened after?

Once, my close friend _____ , which

_____ affected our friendship. I reacted by _____

_____ . After that, (he/she) _____ _____

_____ , and we (are/aren't) _____ friends to this day.

Be an Academic Author

Write
Discuss
Listen

Read the prompt and complete the frames. Strengthen your response with a relevant example. ▶
PROMPT: Think of something that you wanted for your birthday but did not receive and consequently, had to buy for yourself. How did you earn the money?

I really wanted (a/an) _____ _____ for my

birthday, but I did not receive one. _____ , I needed to earn the money to buy it

for myself. One way I earned the money is from _____

_____ .

Construct a Response

Write
Discuss
Listen

Read the prompt and brainstorm ideas for a thoughtful response. Construct a response that includes a relevant example and personal experience. ▶
PROMPT: Everyone has made a mistake and had to face the consequences. Think of a time you did something foolish. What happened and what did you consequently learn?

_____

_____

_____

grammar tip ▶

A **past tense verb** describes an action that already happened. For verbs that end in silent *e*, drop the final *e* before you add *-ed*.

EXAMPLE: The teacher **erased** the whiteboard thoroughly and then **asked** the class to put away their notebooks.

eventually
adverb

Say it: e • **ven** • tu • al • ly

 Write it: _____   **Write it again:** _____

 _____

TOOLKIT

Meaning
happening at the end of a long period of time or complex process

Synonyms
• finally

Antonyms
• initially

Examples
• Over time, a _____ **eventually** becomes a butterfly.

• My dad accidentally left the headlights on after we parked the car at the mall, so **eventually** the _____ died.

Family
• **Adjective:** eventual

Word Partners
• eventually become

• but eventually

Examples
• As a child, Albert Einstein was slow to learn to speak. However, he **eventually became** a Nobel Prize-winning scientist.
• At first, I thought our new coach was too strict, **but eventually** I realized how effective he was.

 Try It

If you practice and have a desire to succeed, you can **eventually** become (a/an) _____ _____ .

VERBAL PRACTICE

Talk about it   Discuss ideas with your partner, listen to classmates, and then write your favorite idea.

Discuss
Listen
Write

1. It took a lot of persuading, but I **eventually** convinced my parents to let me

_____ .

2. I found _____ extremely difficult at first, but I

eventually got the hang of it.

eventually
adverb

WRITING PRACTICE

Collaborate
Discuss
Agree
Write
Listen

Discuss ideas with your partner and agree on the best words to complete the frame. ▶

We waited a long time for the _____ to _____ , but

_____ we decided to _____ .

Our Turn
Discuss
Listen
Write

Read the prompt. Work with the teacher to complete the frames. Write a thoughtful response that includes a relevant example. ▶
PROMPT: Describe the rise to prominence of a historical person or celebrity. What did they start out as? What did they eventually become?

_____ started out as (a/an) _____ _____

_____ , but (he/she) _____ _____ became one of

the most _____ in the world.

Be an Academic Author
Write
Discuss
Listen

Read the prompt and complete the frames. Strengthen your response with a personal experience and a convincing reason. ▶
PROMPT: Describe how you and a friend first met and eventually became close friends.

I first met my friend _____ because we

_____ .

We _____ became very close friends because we _____

_____ .

Construct a Response
Write
Discuss
Listen

Read the prompt and brainstorm ideas for a thoughtful response. Construct a response that includes a personal experience and a convincing reason. ▶
PROMPT: It can be difficult for people to deal with change. Describe an event that changed your life in a significant way. How did you eventually become accustomed to this change?

_____

_____

_____

grammar tip ▶
An **adverb** describes, or tells about, a verb. Adverbs usually end in *-ly*. Occasionally, adverbs come before the verb to describe how the action is done.

EXAMPLE: I **reluctantly** went to the science fiction movie with my brother, but **actually** I enjoyed it.

ultimate
adjective

Say it: **ul** • ti • mate

Write it: _____   **Write it again:** _____

_____

TOOLKIT

Meaning
the most important and last in a list, series, or process

Examples
- After a day of celebrations, the **ultimate** event of the festival is a magnificent _____ .

Synonyms
- greatest; last

Antonyms
- worst; first

- The **ultimate** goal of most high school students is to _____ .

Family
- **Adverb:** ultimately

Word Partners
- someone's ultimate aim/ goal/purpose
- the ultimate outcome of the (experiment/project)

Examples
- My brother is a gifted classical musician, but **his ultimate goal** is to be an orchestra conductor.
- The **ultimate outcome of my mother's eye surgery** was improved vision.

 Try It

My friend and I worked hard to make ——————————————————————————
————————————————— , but the **ultimate** outcome was a big mess.

VERBAL PRACTICE

Talk about it   Discuss ideas with your partner, listen to classmates, and then write your favorite idea.

Discuss
Listen
Write

1. I started a new exercise program with the **ultimate** aim of _____
   _____ .

2. It took me a long time to assemble (a/an) _____ _____
   _____ on craft day, but I was pleased with the **ultimate** outcome.

WRITING PRACTICE

Collaborate

Discuss
Agree
Write
Listen

Discuss ideas with your partner and agree on the best words to complete the frame. ▶

Our class worked together on (a/an) _____ _____ to raise funds.

The _____ outcome of our project was earning enough to purchase

_____ .

Our Turn

Discuss
Listen
Write

Read the prompt. Work with the teacher to complete the frames. Write a thoughtful response that includes a personal experience. ▶

PROMPT: **Sometimes we start learning a basic skill with a bigger goal in mind. What are you learning how to do now? What is your ultimate purpose for learning this skill?**

Right now, I'm learning how to _____ . My _____

purpose is to be able to _____ .

Be an Academic Author

Write
Discuss
Listen

Read the prompt and complete the frames. Strengthen your response with a convincing reason. ▶

PROMPT: **Imagine you and a friend decided to build a clubhouse in the yard. What steps would you need to take, and what do you think the ultimate outcome of the project would be? Why?**

If my friend and I decided to build a clubhouse, our first step would be to _____

_____ , and then we would

have to _____ . I think the

_____ outcome of the project would be _____

because we are both _____ .

Construct a Response

Write
Discuss
Listen

Read the prompt and brainstorm ideas for a thoughtful response. Construct a response that includes a personal experience. ▶

PROMPT: **Think of a time you joined a group or participated in an activity. What was your ultimate aim for joining the group or activity? What was the ultimate outcome?**

_____

_____

_____

grammar tip ▶

An **adjective** describes, or tells about, a noun. Usually an adjective goes before the noun it describes.

EXAMPLE: The **detailed** recipe yielded **excellent** results.

current

REVIEW: resolution   *noun*

DAY 1

We had a dispute with the neighbors because they were _____

_____ , but we have

since reached a peaceful _____ .

☐

☐

---

current   *adjective*

DAY 2

One _____ trend in music is for artists to use

_____ .

☐

☐

DAY 3

I recently discovered _____ , and it has

become my _____ favorite food.

☐

☐

DAY 4

Many Americans don't know enough about _____ events

because they are more interested in _____ .

☐

☐

DAY 5

I would like to send my little cousin a _____ , but

my aunt and uncle moved and I don't know their _____ address.

☐

☐

TOTAL

SMART START

REVIEW: current *adjective*

DAY 1

One _____ TV show I enjoy is _____

_____ .

phase *noun*

DAY 2

When I was little, I went through a _____ in which I was

obsessed with _____ .

DAY 3

The initial _____ of our holiday party preparations involved

_____ .

DAY 4

In temperate climates, the weather goes through various _____ throughout

the year. I most enjoy the time of year when it's _____

_____ .

DAY 5

My uncle is still just in the planning _____ of opening his

own restaurant, but he has already chosen the _____ .

TOTAL

transition

REVIEW: phase   *noun*

DAY 1

Children go through many _____ . For example, during the "terrible twos," after they have started to walk and talk, toddlers are known to _____ .

☐
☐

transition   *noun*

DAY 2

My _____ from elementary school to middle school (was/wasn't) _____ very difficult because _____ .

☐
☐

DAY 3

During the period of _____ from their large suburban house to (a/an) _____ _____ , my grandparents had to get rid of a huge amount of possessions.

☐
☐

DAY 4

When his old car died, my uncle made the _____ from driving to _____ to work.

☐
☐

DAY 5

After our teacher reviewed the first drafts of our _____ , she reminded us to include a smooth _____ from one sentence or idea to another in our writing.

☐
☐

TOTAL

consequently

SMART START

REVIEW: transition   *noun*

DAY 1

The street dog made a remarkable _____ from

_____ to healthy and happy after he was adopted.

consequently   *adverb*

DAY 2

I got a flat tire on the bike trail. _____ , I had to

_____ .

DAY 3

My classmate and I _____ ,

and _____ we both did very well on the science test.

DAY 4

I spilled juice on my report. _____ , I had to

_____ .

DAY 5

My friend forgot her lunch bag at home yesterday, so _____ ,

she _____ .

TOTAL

79

eventually

REVIEW: consequently   *adverb*

DAY 1

Some students didn't listen to the teacher when she told us to settle down, and

_____ she _____

_____ .

☐

☐

---

eventually   *adverb*

DAY 2

Being a scientist would be rewarding, especially if we could _____

discover a way to _____ .

☐

☐

DAY 3

The little boy was throwing a tantrum because he wanted to _____

_____ , but his mother did not

relent, and _____ he cooled down.

☐

☐

DAY 4

My grandfather worked hard all his life, and he _____ became a

successful _____ .

☐

☐

DAY 5

The school year seems like it will last forever, but when it _____ ends, my

friends and I will celebrate by _____ .

☐

☐

TOTAL

🏁 SMART START

REVIEW: eventually *adjective*

DAY 1

It seemed like the _____ would last forever, ☐

but I was relieved when it _____ came to a conclusion. ☐

---

ultimate *adjective*

DAY 2

When we dined at a fancy restaurant once, the _____ ☐

course I was served was _____ . ☐

DAY 3

On the _____ day of summer vacation, I usually ☐

_____ . ☐

DAY 4

My friend practices drawing every day. His _____ goal is to ☐

become very skilled at it and _____ . ☐

DAY 5

If I _____ before I write an essay, ☐

the _____ outcome is usually much better. ☐

TOTAL

Create

Create means to make something.

To **create** a plan, solution, or an explanation you need to think carefully and consider different ways to answer a question.

To **create** stories, poems, and other pieces of writing you need to use your imagination and explore many ideas.

 Find It   Read the sample tasks below and circle the steps that would help you **create** a strong response.

1. Think about the story "Little Red Riding Hood" and write a different ending.
   a. Think of a way for the Wolf and Little Red Riding Hood to become friends.
   b. Change the setting to a city.
   c. Change the color of her cape.

2. Explain the impact that human activity is having on oceans. Include two details to support your answer.
   a. Think of two ways that man-made materials impact the oceans.
   b. Write about the importance of a healthy ocean ecosystem.
   c. Write about ways to clean up the oceans.

Try It   **Create** a plan to convince your school board to start the school day later.

Reasons Why the School Day Should _____ Later.

1. It is _____ for teenagers to fall asleep before 10:00 or 11:00 PM.

2. A lack of sleep has a _____ effect on academic performance.

3. Sleep deprivation can cause psychological issues such as _____ .

4. Lack of sleep is linked to health issues such as _____ .

5. Later start times would likely result in a _____ student absences.

RATE WORD KNOWLEDGE

Circle the number that shows your knowledge of the words you'll use as you create plans, solutions, stories, poems, and other pieces of writing.

6th Grade	7th Grade	BEFORE	8th Grade	AFTER
			RATE IT	
approach	contribution	1 2 3 4	modify	1 2 3 4
generate	develop	1 2 3 4	communicate	1 2 3 4
include	select	1 2 3 4	organize	1 2 3 4
elaborate	integrate	1 2 3 4	preparation	1 2 3 4
plan	solve	1 2 3 4	option	1 2 3 4
design	strategy	1 2 3 4	solution	1 2 3 4

DISCUSSION GUIDE
- Form groups of four.
- Assign letters to each person.
- Each group member takes a turn leading a discussion.
- Prepare to report about one word.

Ⓐ Ⓑ
Ⓓ Ⓒ

DISCUSS WORDS

Discuss how well you know the eighth grade words. Then, report to the class how you rated each word.

GROUP LEADER | **Ask**

So, _____ what do you know
(NAME)

about the word _____ ?

GROUP MEMBERS | **Discuss**

1 = I **don't recognize** the word _____ .

I need to learn what it means.

2 = I **recognize** the word _____ ,

but I need to learn the meaning.

3 = I'm **familiar** with the word _____ .

I think it means _____ .

4 = I **know** the word _____ .

It's a _____ , and it means _____ .
(PART OF SPEECH)

Here is my example sentence: _____ .

REPORTER | **Report Word Knowledge**

Our group gave the word _____ a rating of _____ because _____ .

SET A GOAL AND REFLECT

First, set a vocabulary goal for this unit by selecting at least three words that you plan to thoroughly learn.
At the end of the unit, return to this page and write a reflection about one word you have mastered.

GOAL

During this unit I plan to thoroughly learn the words _____ ,

_____ , and _____ . Increasing my word knowledge will

help me speak and write effectively when I create plans and _____ .

As a result of this unit, I feel most confident about the word _____ .

This is my model sentence: _____

_____ .

REFLECTION

modify
verb

Say it: mod • i • fy

 Write it: _____   **Write it again:** _____

 _____

Meaning
to change something in a small way

Synonyms
• change; alter

Examples
• Antonio **modified** his car so that it would run on used cooking _____ .

• Mary Lynn had to **modify** her negative view of the election after analyzing the _____ data.

Forms
• **Present:**

I/You/We/They	modify
He/She/It	modifies

• **Past:** modified

Family
• **Noun:** modification
• **Adjective:** modified

Word Partners
• modify (my, your, is, her, their, our) behavior
• modify the (something)

Examples
• Huan **modified his behavior** and is now more respectful to adults.

• The game was too difficult for five-year-olds, so they **modified the rules** to allow the children to make several attempts instead of just one.

 Try It

My English teacher complimented me on the rough draft of my short story, but she suggested that I **modify** the _____ just a bit for the final draft.

VERBAL PRACTICE

Talk about it   Discuss ideas with your partner, listen to classmates, and then write your favorite idea.

Discuss
Listen
Write

1. Many dog trainers are able to **modify** a dog's behavior by offering a reward, such as (a/an) _____ _____ .

2. Teachers sometimes **modify** their lesson plans to _____ _____ .

modify
verb

Collaborate

Discuss
Agree
Write
Listen

Discuss ideas with your partner and agree on the best words to complete the frame. ▶

I like to occasionally _____ a dessert recipe by replacing the _____

with _____ .

Our Turn

Discuss
Listen
Write

Read the prompt. Work with the teacher to complete the frames. Write a thoughtful response that includes relevant examples. ▶

PROMPT: **Describe ways that you sometimes modify something you wear or use often, such as a jacket or backpack, to reflect your unique personality.**

I sometimes _____ my _____ by adding

_____ to reflect my unique personality. For example,

having (a/an) _____ _____ on one

would represent my _____ style.

Be an Academic Author

Write
Discuss
Listen

Read the prompt and complete the frames. Strengthen your response with a personal experience.

PROMPT: **Describe a recent event when you had to modify your behavior slightly due to the people who were around you or the situation you were in. Explain how you modified your behavior and why.**

Recently, while I was at (the/a/an) _____ _____ ,

I had to _____ my behavior slightly. In particular, I had to be _____

_____ due to the _____ .

Construct a Response

Write
Discuss
Listen

Read the prompt and brainstorm ideas for a thoughtful response. Construct a response that includes convincing reasons. ▶

PROMPT: **Describe a game or an app you enjoy that you would occasionally like to modify in order to make it easier or more challenging to play.**

_____

_____

_____

_____

grammar tip ▶

An **adverb of frequency** tells how many times something happens. The adverbs *always, usually, sometimes, often, frequently, occasionally,* and *never* can go before or after a verb.

EXAMPLES: Many people **frequently** run near the river. My dog **usually** sleeps for hours.

communicate
verb

Say it: com • **mu** • ni • cate

 Write it: _____ **Write it again:** _____

 _____

TOOLKIT

Meaning
to talk or write to someone

Synonyms
• talk to; write

Examples
• Letters were once the most common way to **communicate** with _____ and family.

• Referees often **communicate** effectively with hand _____ and whistles.

Forms
• **Present:**
  I/You/We/They communicate
  He/She/It   communicates
• **Past:**   communicated

Family
• **Noun:** communication
• **Adjective:** communicative

Word Partners
• ability to communicate

• communicate effectively

Examples
• A successful leader has the **ability to communicate** his or her ideas.
• If you are at a concert, whispering is the best way to **communicate effectively** with the person next to you.

 Try It
Most teenagers I know enjoy having the ability to **communicate** with friends by _____
_____ .

VERBAL PRACTICE

Talk about it

Discuss ideas with your partner, listen to classmates, and then write your favorite idea.

**Discuss
Listen
Write**

1. Great bands and musicians, such as _____ ,

   have the ability to **communicate** their ideas using thought-provoking lyrics.

2. Her older brother quickly returned her toy after the unhappy toddler was able to

   communicate effectively by _____ .

86 Unit 5

communicate

verb

WRITING PRACTICE

Collaborate

Discuss
Agree
Write
Listen

Discuss ideas with your partner and agree on the best words to complete the frame. ▶

Animals like _____ can _____ with each other

using special _____ .

Our Turn

Discuss
Listen
Write

Read the prompt. Work with the teacher to complete the frames. Write a thoughtful response that includes a relevant example. ▶

PROMPT: **Describe one way that the best teachers can communicate effectively.**

The best teachers can _____ effectively using _____

_____ . For example, when my _____

teacher demonstrated how to _____ ,

I felt prepared to accomplish the task.

Be an Academic Author

Write
Discuss
Listen

Read the prompt and complete the frames. Strengthen your response with a convincing reason.

PROMPT: **Describe a new technology that scientists might create that will give them the ability to communicate with an animal, or alien life in the future? What might scientists find out?**

In the future, scientists might create a new technology that would give them the ability to

_____ with (a/an) _____ _____ .

This technology might enable scientists to _____

_____ .

Construct a Response

Write
Discuss
Listen

Read the prompt and brainstorm ideas for a thoughtful response. Construct a response that includes relevant examples. ▶

PROMPT: **Describe how often and the way in which you can communicate effectively with your best friend. What does this friend understand better than anyone else about you?**

_____

_____

_____

grammar tip ▶

Use the **modal verb**, or helping verb, *can* to show that something is possible. When you use *can*, add a verb in the base form.

EXAMPLE: I **can** ride my new bike to school tomorrow. My mom **can** take me to school in the car today.

organize
verb

Say it: **or** • ga • nize

 Write it: _____   **Write it again:** _____

 _____

TOOLKIT

Meaning	**Examples**
to put things in order	• Before going to bed, my sister always **organizes** her _____.
Synonyms	• After the holidays, my aunt helped **organize** all of our _____ before we put them away.
• order; arrange	

Forms
- **Present:**
  I/You/We/They   organize
  He/She/It   organizes
- **Past:**   organized

Family
- **Nouns:** organization, organizer
- **Adjectives:** organized, organizational

Word Partners
- help organize
- able to organize

Examples
- The bus driver asked the passengers to **help organize** the luggage on the curb so he could put it in the storage compartments.
- After donating her old clothes, my sister was finally **able to organize** her closet.

✎ **Try It**
The volunteers carefully **organized** the _____ for the donation to the animal shelter.

VERBAL PRACTICE

Talk about it

    Discuss
    Listen
    Write

Discuss ideas with your partner, listen to classmates, and then write your favorite idea.

1. When packing for a long trip, I usually **organize** my _____ in my

   suitcase last.

2. Last year, my teacher **organized** a field trip to the _____

   _____ .

organize
verb

WRITING PRACTICE

Collaborate

Discuss
Agree
Write
Listen

Discuss ideas with your partner and agree on the best words to complete the frame. ▶

If you _____ your _____ by _____ ,

it will be much easier to find the one you want.

Our Turn

Discuss
Listen
Write

Read the prompt. Work with the teacher to complete the frames. Write a thoughtful response that includes a convincing reason. ▶

PROMPT: Describe a project that you would like students to help organize that would raise funds for an important organization in your community, in the world, or for your school.

It would be ideal for students at our school to help _____ a _____

_____ to raise funds for the _____

_____ . This is an important project because _____

_____ .

Be an Academic Author

Write
Discuss
Listen

Read the prompt and complete the frames. Strengthen your response with a convincing reason. ▶

PROMPT: Describe a set of items, such as photos or notes, that you were able to organize recently. Why was it helpful to have the items organized?

Recently, I was able to _____ my _____ .

This made the tasks I have to do much easier, especially when I wanted to _____

_____ .

Construct a Response

Write
Discuss
Listen

Read the prompt and brainstorm ideas for a thoughtful response. Construct a response that includes relevant examples. ▶

PROMPT: Imagine that you have been asked to help your neighbors organize something, such as a garage or sports equipment. Describe the process you would use to help organize the items.

_____

_____

_____

grammar tip ▶

A **common noun** names a person, place, thing, or idea. **Singular nouns** name one person, place, thing, or idea. The words *a, an, one,* and *the* often appear before a singular noun.

EXAMPLE: The chef will make **an appetizer**, **a pasta** and a **dessert**

preparation
noun

 Write it: _____ **Write it again:** _____

 _____

Meaning
the act of getting something ready to use

Examples
- Moving to a new _____ takes a lot of **preparation**.

Synonyms
- readiness

- The canvases that my sister uses for _____ require a lot of **preparation**.

TOOLKIT

Forms
- **Singular:** preparation
- **Plural:** preparations

Family
- **Verb:** prepare
- **Adjectives:** prepared, preparatory

Word Partners
- adequate preparation

- careful preparation

Examples
- Emily will do fine in advanced algebra because she's had **adequate preparation** in her sixth and seventh grade math classes.
- The **careful preparation** that we put into planning the surprise party will help ensure that it goes smoothly.

 Try It
The **preparation** for our family vacation to _____ is important but also very time consuming.

VERBAL PRACTICE

Talk about it   Discuss ideas with your partner, listen to classmates, and then write your favorite idea.

Discuss
Listen
Write

1. Many people believe that **preparation** for college should begin in _____

_____ .

2. Some students don't do well in _____ class because they

haven't had adequate **preparation**.

WRITING PRACTICE

Collaborate

Discuss
Agree
Write
Listen

Discuss ideas with your partner and agree on the best words to complete the frame. ▶

Our coach said adequate _____ would be the key to next week's

_____ .

Our Turn

Discuss
Listen
Write

Read the prompt. Work with the teacher to complete the frames. Write a thoughtful response that includes a relevant example. ▶

PROMPT: **Imagine that scientists predicted that a natural disaster, like a hurricane or earthquake, might hit your town next month. What careful preparations could you and your classmates make?**

If a natural disaster like (a/an) _____ _____ was predicted

to hit our town, a number of careful _____ would be very beneficial. For

example, the students at our school could _____

_____ .

Be an Academic Author

Write
Discuss
Listen

Read the prompt and complete the frames. Strengthen your response with a convincing reason.

PROMPT: **Describe a time when you thought you had adequate preparation for an important test. However, when you took the exam, you discovered some questions you weren't prepared for.**

Once, I thought I had adequate _____ for (a/an) _____ _____

test. However, the exam included questions about _____

_____ that I should have studied more thoroughly.

Construct a Response

Write
Discuss
Listen

Read the prompt and brainstorm ideas for a thoughtful response. Construct a response that includes relevant examples. ▶

PROMPT: **Imagine that you have to provide a presentation to your class on an activity that you enjoy. Describe tasks that you would accomplish in your preparation for the presentation.**

_____

_____

_____

grammar tip ▶

Use the **modal verb**, or helping verb, *would* to show that something is possible under certain conditions. Use the **modal verb** *could* to show that something might be possible. When you use *would* or *could*, add a verb in the base form.

EXAMPLE: If I won a new bike, I **would** ride it to school, then I **could** show it to my friends.

option
noun

 Write it: _____ **Write it again:** _____

 _____

Meaning a choice between two or more things	**Examples** • Smaller convenience stores usually have fewer **options** to _____ from.
Synonyms choice; alternative	• The little girls considered their **options** for the puzzle by turning the pieces until they _____ .

Forms
- **Singular:** option
- **Plural:** options

Family
- **Verb:** opt
- **Adjective:** optional

Word Partners
- consider (my/your/his /her/ their/our) options
- given the option

Examples
- After receiving three job offers, John Carlos **considered his options** by analyzing the positive and negative aspects of each position.
- When **given the option** of ice cream or cake, I will always choose ice cream.

 Try It

During the cultural fair, students were given the **option** of _____ or _____ for lunch.

VERBAL PRACTICE

Talk about it

Discuss Listen Write

Discuss ideas with your partner, listen to classmates, and then write your favorite idea.

1. Given the **option**, I would rather communicate with my _____ in person.

2. Our teacher gave us two **options** for our _____ .

WRITING PRACTICE

Collaborate

Discuss
Agree
Write
Listen

Discuss ideas with your partner and agree on the best words to complete the frame. ▶

One relaxing _____ I often enjoy during the weekend is to

_____ .

Our Turn

Discuss
Listen
Write

Read the prompt. Work with the teacher to complete the frame. Write a thoughtful response that includes a convincing reason. ▶

PROMPT: **Name two food options that you might be given to eat for lunch. Which would you choose and why?**

Given the _____ to eat (a/an) _____ _____

or _____ for lunch, I would choose _____

_____ . I'd make this choice because it is _____ .

Be an Academic Author

Write
Discuss
Listen

Read the prompt and complete the frames. Strengthen your response with relevant examples. ▶

PROMPT: **Imagine that you have a big decision to make. When you consider your options, what do you typically do next? How are these steps helpful in your decision making process?**

When I have to make a big decision, I consider my _____ carefully. Then I

_____ .

These steps help my decision making process because I can _____

_____ .

Construct a Response

Write
Discuss
Listen

Read the prompt and brainstorm ideas for a thoughtful response. Construct a response that includes a convincing reason. ▶

PROMPT: **When it comes to weekend activities, is it better to have many options, or is it better to have just a few? Why?**

_____

_____

_____

grammar tip ▶

A **common noun** names a person, place, thing, or idea. **Singular nouns** name one person, place, thing, or idea. The words *a*, *an*, *one*, and *the* often appear before a singular noun.

EXAMPLE: **The tortoise** ate **the raspberry** and **a stalk** of celery.

solution
noun

 Write it: _____   **Write it again:** _____

 _____

Meaning
an answer to a problem

Examples
- If you have trouble sleeping, sticking to a _____ is one possible **solution**.

Synonyms
- answer

- Blanca offered several **solutions** to the _____ equation.

Forms
- **Singular:** solution
- **Plural:** solutions

Family
- **Verb:** solve
- **Adjective:** solvable

Word Partners
- find (a/the) solution

- solution to the problem

Examples
- To **find the solution** to this math problem, you have to know how to multiply fractions.
- The latest update should provide the **solution to the problem** he is having with the software.

 Try It

When the _____ was invented, it offered people a **solution** to the problem of long-distance transportation.

VERBAL PRACTICE

Talk about it   Discuss ideas with your partner, listen to classmates, and then write your favorite idea.

Discuss
Listen
Write

1. If a student is always late for class, I think one possible **solution** is for the teacher to _____ .

2. There is no easy **solution** to the problem of _____ .

WRITING PRACTICE

Collaborate

Discuss
Agree
Write
Listen

Discuss ideas with your partner and agree on the best words to complete the frame. ▶

After tasting the bland cake batter, we found a _____ , which was to add some

_____ to the bowl.

Our Turn

Discuss
Listen
Write

Read the prompt. Work with the teacher to complete the frames. Write a thoughtful response that includes a convincing reason. ▶

PROMPT: **Describe one major problem in the word for which you would like to find a solution.**

If I could find a _____ to one major problem in the world, I would want to

_____ . In my opinion, if this problem

was solved, people would be able to _____ .

Be an Academic Author

Write
Discuss
Listen

Read the prompt and complete the frames. Strengthen your response with a personal experience. ▶

PROMPT: **Some problems have simple solutions. Describe something minor, like being thirsty or forgetting your homework, and the simple solution to the problem.**

A simple _____ to the problem of _____

_____ is to _____ . Recently,

I was _____ , so I decided to

_____ .

Construct a Response

Write
Discuss
Listen

Read the prompt and brainstorm ideas for a thoughtful response. Construct a response that includes relevant examples. ▶

PROMPT: **Describe a rewarding experience you have had working with a group of students to find a solution to a problem.**

_____

_____

_____

grammar tip ▶

An **adjective** describes, or tells about, a noun. Adjectives are always singular even if they describe a plural noun. Do not add **-s** to adjectives that describe plural nouns.

EXAMPLE: My **old** cat enjoys sleeping on **warm** blankets and eating **soft** treats.

modify

REVIEW: **ultimate**   *adjective*

DAY 1

My uncle bought a large amount of lumber from the home improvement store with the

_____ aim of _____

_____ .

☐

☐

modify   *verb*

DAY 2

I recently _____ my backpack by adding

_____ to customize and personalize it.

☐

☐

DAY 3

When we learned that _____

_____ , we had to _____ our weekend plans accordingly.

☐

☐

DAY 4

My friend used to have trouble _____ ,

but he _____ his study habits and is doing much better now.

☐

☐

DAY 5

After my grandfather's quadruple bypass surgery, he had to drastically

_____ his _____ .

☐

☐

TOTAL

SMART START

REVIEW: modify   *verb*

DAY 1

When she was little, my cousin was almost always _____

_____ , but she has drastically _____

her behavior as she has matured.

☐

☐

---

communicate   *verb*

DAY 2

The method I most often use to _____ with my friends is

_____ .

☐

☐

DAY 3

In order to _____ effectively with someone whose first language is

not English, you need to use _____ .

☐

☐

DAY 4

Especially with people we know well, we often have the ability to _____

our feelings through _____ instead of words.

☐

☐

DAY 5

Having (a/an) _____ _____ is

very helpful for _____ with more people around the world.

☐

☐

TOTAL

organize

REVIEW: communicate *verb*

DAY 1

If you want to _____ your ideas effectively in writing, you

need to perfect basic skills like _____ .

☐
☐

organize *verb*

DAY 2

In my bedroom, I have several _____ to help me

_____ my things.

☐
☐

DAY 3

My friend is never able to _____ her _____

_____ . It's a mess!

☐
☐

DAY 4

I would like to help _____ a club at school for students who

enjoy _____ .

☐
☐

DAY 5

After doing research or a survey, you can _____ the data

you've collected by putting it into a _____ .

☐
☐

TOTAL

 **SMART** *START*

REVIEW: organize *verb*

DAY 1

Some people _____ the clothes in their closets according

to _____ .

☐

☐

---

preparation *noun*

DAY 2

Going on a trip requires adequate _____ , which includes steps such as

_____ .

☐

☐

DAY 3

I hadn't done adequate _____ for my oral report, so I

_____ while standing in front of the class.

☐

☐

DAY 4

My mother's complicated _____ had taken hours, so she

was devastated when the _____ slipped

from her hands and fell to the floor.

☐

☐

DAY 5

Despite their rigorous and thorough _____ , the debate team failed to

outdo the _____ of their rivals.

☐

☐

TOTAL

option

REVIEW: preparation   *noun*

DAY 1

Usually, _____ for the first day of the school year include

_____ .

option   *noun*

DAY 2

Given all the _____ available for elective classes in high

school, I will probably take _____ .

DAY 3

It's still early to be considering my career _____ , but I'm

thinking about learning how to _____ .

DAY 4

I knew I was wrong when I _____

_____ , so my only real

_____ was to apologize for it.

DAY 5

Given the usual _____ in a vending machine, I would most

likely pick _____ for a snack.

TOTAL

REVIEW: option *noun*

DAY 1

I missed the bus home from school, so my only _____ was

to _____ .

☐
☐

solution *noun*

DAY 2

I suggested some potential _____ to my friend's problem

with her _____ , but she didn't listen to any of my advice.

☐
☐

DAY 3

The _____ problem seemed complex, but the

_____ was really quite simple.

☐
☐

DAY 4

If you're having trouble motivating yourself to _____

_____ , one _____ might be to find a

buddy who is interested in doing the same thing so you can motivate each other.

☐
☐

DAY 5

To get me to eat more vegetables when I was younger, my mother's _____

was to _____ .

☐
☐

TOTAL

Compare and Contrast

To **compare** two or more things, analyze what is the same.

To **contrast** two or more things, analyze what is different.

 Find It **Compare** paper books and e-readers and circle what is the same.

Paper Books and E-readers

- are used for reading

- use ink

- have a screen

 Try It **Contrast** what is different about paper books and e-readers by adding ideas to each list.

Paper Books	E-readers
• need space to store	• can store hundreds of books in very little space
• are not interactive	• are interactive
• never need to be _____	• occasionally need to be _____

RATE WORD KNOWLEDGE

Circle the number that shows your knowledge of the words you'll use to compare and contrast.

6th Grade	7th Grade	BEFORE	8th Grade	AFTER
differ	advantage	1 2 3 4	**aspect**	1 2 3 4
equivalent	compatible	1 2 3 4	**comparable**	1 2 3 4
distinguish	correspond	1 2 3 4	**draw**	1 2 3 4
contrast	distinguish	1 2 3 4	**distinction**	1 2 3 4
share	problematic	1 2 3 4	**comparison**	1 2 3 4
distinct	viewpoint	1 2 3 4	**direct**	1 2 3 4

RATE IT

DISCUSSION GUIDE
- Form groups of four.
- Assign letters to each person.
- Each group member takes a turn leading a discussion.
- Prepare to report about one word.

Ⓐ Ⓑ
Ⓓ Ⓒ

DISCUSS WORDS

Discuss how well you know the eighth grade words. Then, report to the class how you rated each word.

GROUP LEADER **Ask**

So, _____ what do you know
         (NAME)

about the word _____ ?

GROUP MEMBERS **Discuss**

1 = I **don't recognize** the word _____ .

   I need to learn what it means.

2 = I **recognize** the word _____ ,

   but I need to learn the meaning.

3 = I'm **familiar** with the word _____ .

   I think it means _____ .

4 = I **know** the word _____ .

   It's a _____ , and it means _____ .
           (PART OF SPEECH)

   Here is my example sentence: _____ .

REPORTER **Report Word Knowledge**

Our group gave the word _____ a rating of _____ because _____ .

SET A GOAL AND REFLECT

First, set a vocabulary goal for this unit by selecting at least three words that you plan to thoroughly learn. At the end of the unit, return to this page and write a reflection about one word you have mastered.

GOAL

During this unit I plan to thoroughly learn the words _____ ,

_____ , and _____ . Increasing my word knowledge will

help me speak and write effectively when I compare and _____ .

As a result of this unit, I feel most confident about the word _____ .

This is my model sentence: _____

_____ .

REFLECTION

aspect
noun

 Write it: _____   **Write it again:** _____

 _____

Meaning
a particular feature or part of something

Synonyms
• feature, part

Examples
• One **aspect** of camping I especially enjoy is sitting around the _____ .

• I love many **aspects** of _____ , especially the foliage.

Forms
• **Singular:** aspect
• **Plural:** aspects

Word Partners
• examine/explore/discuss different/similar aspects of
• (all/several/many) aspects of

Examples
• In the surrealism exhibit at the art museum, we **examined similar aspects of** paintings by various artists during the same time period.
• The police noticed that **several aspects of** the two crimes were strikingly similar, leading them to believe that the same person was responsible.

 Try It

An important **aspect** of a healthy lifestyle is _____ .

VERBAL PRACTICE

Talk about it

Discuss
Listen
Write

Discuss ideas with your partner, listen to classmates, and then write your favorite idea.

1. Before making a decision about where to _____ , my older sister examined all the positive and negative **aspects** of each place.

2. My best friend and I have wardrobes with similar **aspects**, such as our _____

   _____ .

WRITING PRACTICE

Collaborate

Discuss
Agree
Write
Listen

Discuss ideas with your partner and agree on the best words to complete the frame. ▶

One of the most exciting _____ of space exploration is that people might be

able to _____ one day.

Our Turn

Discuss
Listen
Write

Read the prompt. Work with the teacher to complete the frames. Write a thoughtful response that includes a relevant example and personal experience. ▶

PROMPT: **Think of an activity you participate in regularly. What are some aspects you enjoy about this activity? What is one aspect that you don't enjoy?**

One activity I regularly participate in is _____ . There are

several _____ of this activity that I enjoy, such as _____

_____ . However, one _____ that I

don't particularly enjoy is _____ .

Be an Academic Author

Write
Discuss
Listen

Read the prompt and complete the frames. Strengthen your response with a relevant example. ▶

PROMPT: **Name a person you admire. Why? Do you share any personality aspects with this person?**

I sincerely admire _____ for (his/her) _____

_____ .

One similar _____ of my personality that I share with this person is that I

_____ .

Construct a Response

Write
Discuss
Listen

Read the prompt and brainstorm ideas for a thoughtful response. Construct a response that includes a relevant example. ▶

PROMPT: **Two stories can be quite different but still share some similar aspects. Choose two different books or movies that are significant for you. What similar aspects do they share?**

_____

_____

_____

grammar tip ▶

Plural nouns name more than one person, place, thing, or idea. The words *some* and *many* often appear before a plural noun.

EXAMPLE: One of my favorite **places** to go is the library because it has so many interesting **books**.

comparable
adjective

com • pa • ra • ble

Say it: com • pa • ra • ble

Write it: _____   **Write it again:** _____

_____

TOOLKIT

Meaning similar in some way to another thing so that they are easy to compare	**Examples** • The simulator ride is **comparable** with the real _____ of driving a car.
Synonyms • similar **Antonyms** • incomparable; unlike	• Today's computers are barely **comparable** to _____ of the past.

Family
- **Noun:** comparison
- **Verb:** compare
- **Adverb:** comparably

Word Partners
- be comparable in _____ (size, price, appearance, etc.)
- comparable to/with

Examples
- My sisters **are comparable in appearance**, but one is two years older and a little taller than the other.
- My mother designs and sews clothes that are **comparable to** ones you can buy in an expensive fashion boutique.

 Try It

A tennis ball and (a/an) _____ _____ are **comparable** in size and shape.

VERBAL PRACTICE

Talk about it

Discuss
Listen
Write

Discuss ideas with your partner, listen to classmates, and then write your favorite idea.

1. At a recent sleepover, my friend's snoring was **comparable** to the sound of a _____
   _____ .

2. An activity that is **comparable** to running in terms of cardio benefits is _____
   _____ .

comparable

adjective

Collaborate

Discuss
Agree
Write
Listen

Discuss ideas with your partner and agree on the best words to complete the frame. ▶

A new _____ is _____ in price with (a/an) _____

_____ .

Our Turn

Discuss
Listen
Write

Read the prompt. Work with the teacher to complete the frames. Write a thoughtful response that includes a convincing reason. ▶

PROMPT: We often share similar characteristics with people in our family. Who do you share a common physical or personality trait with? Why would you say you are comparable?

My _____ and I are _____ in our

_____ . I say this because we both _____

_____ .

Be an Academic Author

Write
Discuss
Listen

Read the prompt and complete the frames. Strengthen your response with a relevant example. ▶

PROMPT: Name a creative person that you know and what they create at home, such as cupcakes or soap. How are the items they create comparable to something that is popular and commercially available?

My _____ homemade _____

are _____ to the ones you can find at (a/an) _____ _____

_____ . They are extremely _____ !

Construct a Response

Write
Discuss
Listen

Read the prompt and brainstorm ideas for a thoughtful response. Construct a response that includes a relevant example and a convincing reason. ▶

PROMPT: Think of two different people or things you have strong feelings about. In what way are your feelings toward them comparable, and why?

_____

_____

_____

grammar tip ▶

An **adjective** describes, or tells about, a noun. An adjective sometimes appears after verbs such as *is, are, look, feel, smell,* and *taste.*

EXAMPLE: All of the players on the softball team are **competent**, but only a **couple** players are **extraordinary**.

draw
verb

 Write it: _____   **Write it again:** _____

 _____

Meaning to show	**Examples** • The inference we **drew** from the _____ in the snow was that our neighbor's dog had been on our porch last night.	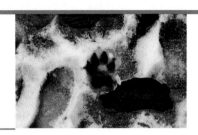
Synonyms • make; show	• At the supermarket, we **drew** comparisons between the wild and farm-raised _____ .	

Forms
- **Present:**
  - I/You/We/They   draw
  - He/She/It   draws
- **Past:**   drew

Word Partners
- draw a comparison between

- draw a distinction between

Examples
- In English class, we **drew comparisons between** many different adaptations and versions of the *Romeo and Juliet* story.
- When I was little, I learned to **draw a distinction between** when our dog's growls showed genuine annoyance and when he was just playing.

 Try It

If we **draw** a comparison between El Salvador and Guatemala, we can point out that _____
_____ .

TOOLKIT

VERBAL PRACTICE

Talk about it   Discuss ideas with your partner, listen to classmates, and then write your favorite idea.

Discuss
Listen
Write

1. It's easy to **draw** comparisons between baseball and _____ .

2. If I were to **draw** one distinction between sharks and dolphins, I'd point out that

_____ .

draw
verb

WRITING PRACTICE

Collaborate

Discuss
Agree
Write
Listen

Discuss ideas with your partner and agree on the best words to complete the frame. ▶

Our nature hike leader _____ distinctions between different types of

_____ to teach us how to identify them.

Our Turn

Discuss
Listen
Write

Read the prompt. Work with the teacher to complete the frames. Write a thoughtful response that includes a convincing reason.
PROMPT: How does a good math teacher approach his or her students? Does he or she draw distinctions between them based on superficial factors?

A good math teacher does not _____ distinctions between students based

on superficial factors such as _____ because this

would be unfair. He or she should give all students an equal opportunity to show they can

_____ .

Be an Academic Author

Write
Discuss
Listen

Read the prompt and complete the frames. Strengthen your response with a relevant example. ▶
PROMPT: Think of two animals that have similar traits. If you drew a comparison between them, what traits would you point to? What distinction could you draw?

If I _____ a comparison between a _____ and a

_____ , I would point out that they _____

_____ . One distinction I could _____ is that _____

_____ .

Construct a Response

Write
Discuss
Listen

Read the prompt and brainstorm ideas for a thoughtful response. Construct a response that includes a relevant example and personal experience. ▶
PROMPT: We often compare ourselves to others when we first meet them. What comparisons did you draw between you and a friend when you first met? What inferences did you draw?

_____

_____

_____

grammar tip ▶

A **past tense verb** describes an action that already happened. Some verbs are irregular and change their spelling to form the past tense, such as *come* and *came*; *begin* and *began*; *draw* and *drew*.

EXAMPLE: When the teacher **came** into the room, we **began** the exam.

draw 109

distinction
noun

Say it: dis • **tinc** • tion

 Write it: _____   **Write it again:** _____

 _____

TOOLKIT

Meaning a clear difference or separation	**Examples** • In some _____ of birds, there is a clear **distinction** between the male and female.

Synonyms • difference, contrast **Antonyms** • similarity, comparison	• Safety devices will protect the toddler who has yet to learn to make **distinctions** between safe and _____ objects.

Forms
- **Singular:** distinction
- **Plural:** distinctions

Family
- **Adjective:** distinct
- **Adverb:** distinctly

Word Partners
- make (important/key/major) distinctions between
- there is a (clear/sharp) distinction between

Examples
- A medical article I read **made major distinctions between** treatments prescribed by doctors and non-science-based alternative remedies.
- Our English teacher explained that **there is a clear distinction between** the words *its* and *it's* so that we would understand when to use each one.

 Try It

There is an important **distinction** between being *assertive*, which is showing confidence, and being *aggressive*, which is acting in a _____ way.

VERBAL PRACTICE

Talk about it

Discuss
Listen
Write

Discuss ideas with your partner, listen to classmates, and then write your favorite idea.

1. One key **distinction** between orange juice and orange soda is that one is _____

   _____ .

2. My friend's and my _____ were so similar, we had to put

   them side by side to notice the **distinctions** between them!

110   Unit 6

distinction

noun

Collaborate

Discuss
Agree
Write
Listen

Discuss ideas with your partner and agree on the best words to complete the frame. ▶

The restaurant menu made clear _____ between _____

items and those that were _____ .

Our Turn

Discuss
Listen
Write

Read the prompt. Work with the teacher to complete the frames. Write a thoughtful response that includes a relevant example. ▶

PROMPT: **When writing a research paper, there is a sharp distinction between consulting a source for information and stealing someone's ideas. What is the distinction and how can you avoid it?**

There is a sharp _____ between using a text as a source and directly

copying words without giving the writer credit. It's better to consult several

_____ and adapt ideas into your own words. Always include

_____ to show where the information came from.

Be an Academic Author

Write
Discuss
Listen

Read the prompt and complete the frames. Strengthen your response with a convincing reason.

PROMPT: **People from different countries or regions speak English with different accents. Is it easy or difficult for you to make distinctions between regional accents? Why?**

For me, it's (easy/hard) _____ to make a _____ between

_____ and _____ accents. This is because

they sound very _____ to me.

Construct a Response

Write
Discuss
Listen

Read the prompt and brainstorm ideas for a thoughtful response. Construct a response that includes a relevant example and personal experience. ▶

PROMPT: **Think of a time when a friend was angry with you because he/she misinterpreted your behavior. In your explanation to him/her, what important distinction did you make?**

_____

_____

_____

grammar tip ▶

A **past tense verb** describes an action that already happened. Some verbs are irregular and change their spelling to form the past tense, such as *come* and *came*; *begin* and *began*; *draw* and *drew*.

EXAMPLE: When I **saw** my mother's face, I **knew** immediately that she was worried.

comparison
noun

Say it: com • **pa** • ri • son

Write it: _____ **Write it again:** _____

_____

TOOLKIT

Meaning a study of the way that two things are the same and different	**Examples** • John is very tall in **comparison** to his _____ . 
	• The scientists made a **comparison** between this _____ and one that caused a flood last year. 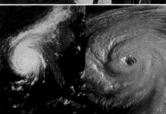

Forms
- **Singular:** comparison
- **Plural:** comparisons

Family
- **Verb:** compare
- **Adjective:** comparable
- **Adverb:** comparatively

Word Partners
- in comparison to
- draw/make a comparison between

Examples
- My bedroom is small **in comparison to** my parent's bedroom.
- It's easy to **draw a comparison between** identical twins.

 Try It

In **comparison** to a news article, (a/an) _____ _____ is very long.

VERBAL PRACTICE

Talk about it Discuss ideas with your partner, listen to classmates, and then write your favorite idea.

Discuss
Listen
Write

1. In my opinion, in **comparison** to Ariana Grande, _____

   is a far better singer.

2. Many shoppers like to _____ to make

   comparisons before making a purchase.

comparison

noun

Collaborate

Discuss
Agree
Write
Listen

Discuss ideas with your partner and agree on the best words to complete the frame. ▶

Our science teacher asked students to make a _____ between _____

_____ and _____ .

Our Turn

Discuss
Listen
Write

Read the prompt. Work with the teacher to complete the frames. Write a thoughtful response that includes a relevant example. ▶

PROMPT: **Describe comparisons that people might make between you and someone else. Provide two things you have in common.**

People might make _____ between me and my _____

because we both _____ . In addition, we both also

have _____ in common.

Be an Academic Author

Write
Discuss
Listen

Read the prompt and complete the frames. Strengthen your response with a relevant example. ▶

PROMPT: **Describe two animals that are easy to draw comparisons between, such as turtles and tortoises. What do they have in common and what is different between them?**

It's easy to draw _____ between _____ and

_____ because they both _____ .

However, what is different is that _____ are _____

_____ .

Construct a Response

Write
Discuss
Listen

Read the prompt and brainstorm ideas for a thoughtful response. Include a personal experience to strengthen your response. ▶

PROMPT: **Describe two sports that are easy to make comparisons between, such as soccer and hockey. What do the two sports have in common and what is different between them?**

_____

_____

_____

grammar tip ▶

Count nouns name things that can be counted, such as a person, place, thing, or idea. Count nouns have two forms, singular and plural. To make most count nouns plural, add **-s**. To make count nouns that end in *x, ch, sh, ss,* and *z* plural, add **-es**.

EXAMPLE: He likes to play video **games** and play **cards** on rainy **days**.

direct
adjective

Say it: di • **rect**

 Write it: _____ **Write it again:** _____

 _____

TOOLKIT

Meaning
exact or immediate, with no other person or thing involved in the process

Synonyms
• complete; total

Antonyms
• indirect

Examples
• The _____ on my bike was a **direct** result of leaving it outside all year and not taking care of it.

• In **direct** contrast to the instructions, my brother overheated the oven and _____ the croissants.

Family
• **Adverb:** directly

Word Partners
• make a direct comparison

• to be in direct contrast to

Examples
• By putting the fundraising data into a bar graph, it was easy to **make a direct comparison** between what we earned this year vs. last year.
• The flimsy, ill-made shirt I received in the mail **was in direct contrast to** the attractive, stylish one pictured on the website I ordered it from.

 Try It
The children's _____ reaction to the puppet show I put on for them was in **direct** contrast to what I had expected.

VERBAL PRACTICE

Talk about it   Discuss ideas with your partner, listen to classmates, and then write your favorite idea.

Discuss
Listen
Write

1. There is a **direct** link between _____

   and poor health.

2. If you make a **direct** side-by-side comparison between an authentic _____

   _____ and a cheap copy, it's easy

   to tell them apart.

WRITING PRACTICE

Collaborate

Discuss
Agree
Write
Listen

Discuss ideas with your partner and agree on the best words to complete the frame. ▶

If we make a _____ comparison of _____ and _____ _____ music, we see that both music styles are quite _____ .

Our Turn

Discuss
Listen
Write

Read the prompt. Work with the teacher to complete the frames. Write a thoughtful response that includes a personal experience and convincing reason. ▶
PROMPT: Have you made a direct comparison between a homemade food or drink and a processed version from the store? Which do you prefer?

I have made a _____ comparison between fresh, homemade _____

_____ and a processed version from the store. The _____

_____ one is clearly superior because it's much more _____ .

Be an Academic Author

Write
Discuss
Listen

Read the prompt and complete the frames. Strengthen your response with a personal experience. ▶
PROMPT: Think of a time you went to an event, a performance, or a movie, and it defied your expectations. How was the experience in direct contrast to what you had thought it would be?

My impressions of _____

_____ were in _____ contrast to my

expectations. I was sure it would be _____ , but I actually found

it quite _____ .

Construct a Response

Write
Discuss
Listen

Read the prompt and brainstorm ideas for a thoughtful response. Construct a response that includes a relevant example. ▶
PROMPT: Is there always a direct connection between what a person studies and what they later do for a job? Think of someone in your family. What do they do for a living? What did they study?

_____

_____

_____

grammar tip ▶

An **adjective** describes, or tells about, a noun. Usually an adjective goes before the noun it describes.

EXAMPLE: Someone wrote an **unfavorable** review of my **favorite** restaurant on this **touristic** website.

aspect

SMARTSTART

REVIEW: **solution** *noun*

DAY 1

As hard as we tried, we couldn't come up with the _____

to the _____ , so we looked it up in the

answer key.

---

aspect *noun*

DAY 2

One _____ of school that I enjoy is

_____ .

DAY 3

In social studies class, we explored different _____ of ancient Egyptian

culture, such as their writing system and their _____ .

DAY 4

Although one of the positive _____ of spending time on social media is

that you can stay connected to so many people, one downside is that you can end up

_____

_____ .

DAY 5

An _____ of living in my neighborhood that I appreciate

is having _____ .

TOTAL

⚑ SMART START

REVIEW: aspect *noun*

DAY 1

Recently, our teacher explained several _____ of our government, such as

how _____ . ☐ ☐

comparable *adjective*

DAY 2

Skateboarding is _____ to _____ , ☐

because they both require skill and balance. ☐

DAY 3

My friend and his father are _____ in appearance because ☐

they both have _____ . ☐

DAY 4

A _____ is _____ in size and ☐

shape to a volleyball. ☐

DAY 5

Spaghetti is _____ to _____ in ☐

texture and appearance. ☐

TOTAL

draw

REVIEW: comparable *adjective*

DAY 1

For me, ice cream and _____ are

_____ in terms of how much I enjoy eating them.

draw *verb*

DAY 2

One parallel that people sometimes _____ between me and

my best friend is that we _____ .

DAY 3

In order to _____ a comparison between two similar

_____ , I held them side by side at the store.

DAY 4

I can _____ many major distinctions between our new TV and

our old one. For example, our new TV is much _____ .

DAY 5

When I saw _____

_____ , the first inference I _____ was that the

cat had eaten the rest of the leftover pie.

TOTAL

 **SMART** *START*

REVIEW: draw *verb*

DAY 1

When all of the _____ in the mystery pointed to one

character early on in the story, I _____ the conclusion that

this character probably wasn't the culprit because it was too obvious. ☐ ☐

---

distinction *noun*

DAY 2

One major _____ between a penguin and a toucan is that

a toucan _____ . ☐ ☐

DAY 3

If I were to draw a clear _____ between a democracy and

(a/an) _____ _____ , I would point out that in a

democracy the people choose their leaders and have the freedom to criticize them. ☐ ☐

DAY 4

There is a key _____ between telling a little white lie in

order to _____

and telling a big lie meant to deceive or mislead someone. ☐ ☐

DAY 5

Learning _____ helps you make comparisons

and _____ between words in the same word family. ☐ ☐

TOTAL

comparison

REVIEW: distinction *noun*

DAY 1

When parents make rules for their children, they need to make clear _____

between behavior that is acceptable and behavior that is _____

_____ .

---

comparison *noun*

DAY 2

A cabin in the woods can be quite _____ in

_____ to an apartment in the city.

DAY 3

In _____ to my friend's handwriting, mine is much

_____ .

DAY 4

Try not to draw too many _____ between yourself and other

people because it can sometimes make you feel _____

unnecessarily.

DAY 5

In English class, we made _____ between several

_____ from various cultures around the world.

TOTAL

120

![SMART START]

REVIEW: comparison   *noun*

One _____ you could draw between a fox and a dog is that

they are both _____ .

☐
☐

direct   *adjective*

The food at the new restaurant was _____ , in

_____ contrast to what I expected, based on the colorful,

artsy decor and exciting menu design.

☐
☐

My father enjoys shopping online because it's easier to make _____

comparisons between products from different _____ .

☐
☐

In _____ contrast to her mother's instructions to go straight

home and do her chores, my classmate _____

_____ after school.

☐
☐
☐

In my experience, there is a _____ link between

_____ and feeling relaxed.

☐
☐

TOTAL

Inference

To make an **inference**, use a picture or information from the text and what we already know to form an idea.

🔍 Find It   Look at the picture above. Answer each question and make an **inference**.

What do you already know?	+	What has happened in the picture?	=	My inference
I already know that riding a skateboard well is a skill that takes a lot of practice and experience.		The girl is doing a very _____ move with her skateboard.		I think the girl is a very _____ skateboarder.

✏️ Try It   Read the headline from the newspaper. Answer each question and make an **inference**.

Health Risks Associated with Soda Consumption

What do you already know?	+	What does the headline mean?	=	My inference
I already know that soda is not _____ .		The headline means that specific health risks are linked with _____ .		So this means I should not drink soda or at least cut back on it in order to avoid _____ .

RATE WORD KNOWLEDGE

Rate how well you know Toolkit words you'll use when you make inferences.

6th Grade	7th Grade	BEFORE	8th Grade	AFTER
determine	conclusion	1 2 3 4	expand	1 2 3 4
logical	prediction	1 2 3 4	perceive	1 2 3 4
generalize	assumption	1 2 3 4	generalization	1 2 3 4
involve	infer	1 2 3 4	perception	1 2 3 4
generalization	imply	1 2 3 4	presume	1 2 3 4
assume	interpretation	1 2 3 4	conclusion	1 2 3 4

RATE IT

DISCUSSION GUIDE
- Form groups of four.
- Assign letters to each person. Ⓐ Ⓑ Ⓓ Ⓒ
- Each group member takes a turn leading a discussion.
- Prepare to report about one word.

DISCUSS WORDS

Discuss how well you know the eighth grade words. Then, report to the class how you rated each word.

GROUP LEADER **Ask**

So, _____ what do you know
(NAME)

about the word _____ ?

GROUP MEMBERS **Discuss**

1 = I **don't recognize** the word _____ .

I need to learn what it means.

2 = I **recognize** the word _____ ,

but I need to learn the meaning.

3 = I'm **familiar** with the word _____ .

I think it means _____ .

4 = I **know** the word _____ .

It's a _____ , and it means _____ .
(PART OF SPEECH)

Here is my example sentence: _____ .

REPORTER **Report Word Knowledge**

Our group gave the word _____ a rating of _____ because _____ .

SET A GOAL AND REFLECT

First, set a vocabulary goal for this unit by selecting at least three words that you plan to thoroughly learn.
At the end of the unit, return to this page and write a reflection about one word you have mastered.

GOAL

During this unit I plan to thoroughly learn the words _____ ,

_____ , and _____ . Increasing my word knowledge will

help me speak and write effectively when I make an _____ .

As a result of this unit, I feel most confident about the word _____ .

This is my model sentence: _____

_____ .

REFLECTION

expand
verb

 Say it: ex • pand

 Write it: _____ **Write it again:** _____

_____

TOOLKIT

Meaning
to explain or add more details

Examples
- The reporter asked the candidate to **expand** on her _____ .

Synonyms
- elaborate

- Near the end of class, the _____ **expanded** upon the purpose of our experiment.

Forms
- **Present:**
  I/You/We/They   expand
  He/She/It   expands
- **Past:** expanded

Family
- **Noun:** expansion
- **Verb:** expand (to grow larger, or increase in size)
- **Adjective:** expansive

Word Partners
- expand on/upon (something)
- begin/continue to expand on

Examples
- Scientists decided to **expand upon their research** by studying the effects of the drought over several years.
- The teacher asked the students to **continue to expand on** key points from the discussion in their essays.

 Try It
After reading the directions, I decided to **expand** on the recipe by adding some _____
_____ .

VERBAL PRACTICE

Talk about it

Discuss
Listen
Write

Discuss ideas with your partner, listen to classmates, and then write your favorite idea.

1. When writing (a/an) _____ _____ , it is important to

   expand on your ideas by adding details.

2. My friend and I looked for my _____ for

   thirty minutes before deciding to **expand** on the list of places where I might have left it.

WRITING PRACTICE

Collaborate

Discuss
Agree
Write
Listen

Discuss ideas with your partner and agree on the best words to complete the frame. ▶

After she read a brief article about _____ ,

my cousin _____ her understanding by doing additional research online.

Our Turn

Discuss
Listen
Write

Read the prompt. Work with the teacher to complete the frames. Write a thoughtful response that includes a relevant example.
PROMPT: **Identify a job, such as astronaut or shoe designer, that you find interesting. How could you expand on your understanding of the skills required to obtain this job?**

From my perspective, being (a/an) _____ _____

_____ seems interesting because you get to _____

_____ . One way I can _____ on my understanding

of the skills required for this job is to _____ .

Be an Academic Author

Write
Discuss
Listen

Read the prompt and complete the frames. Strengthen your response with a personal experience. ▶
PROMPT: **Describe a time when you broke an object and you had to explain what happened to its owner. How did you expand upon your explanation? How did they react to your explanation?**

Once, I had to explain to my _____ how I broke (a/an/the) _____

_____ . I _____ on my

explanation by _____ .

Eventually, (he/she) _____ reacted by _____ .

Construct a Response

Write
Discuss
Listen

Read the prompt and brainstorm ideas for a thoughtful response. Include a relevant example to strengthen your response.
PROMPT: **Imagine that you are assigned to a group project and your classmate needs help writing their portion of the assignment. How will you help them expand on their ideas?**

_____

_____

_____

grammar tip ▶

A **past tense verb** describes an action that already happened. Some verbs are irregular and change their spelling to form the past tense, such as *come* and *came*; *feed* and *fed*; *eat* and *ate*.

EXAMPLE: Isabel **fed** her cat after she **came** home from school. The cat **ate** every morsel.

perceive
verb

Say it: per • ceive

 Write it: _____   **Write it again:** _____

 _____

Meaning	Examples
to understand or think about something in a certain way	• Many track athletes **perceive** throwing the discus as a very _____ skill. 
Synonyms • know, grasp	• High school students who **perceive** themselves as _____ are more likely to apply to college. 

Forms
- **Present:**
  | I/You/We/They | perceive |
  | He/She/It | perceives |
- **Past:** perceived

Family
- **Noun:** perception
- **Adjectives:** perceptive, perceptible
- **Adverbs:** perceivably, perceptively

Word Partners
- perceive (something) differently
- perceive myself/themselves

Examples
- Do you think men **perceive the world differently** than women?
- Very few people **perceive themselves** as dishonest.

 Try It

I **perceive** most working adults to be _____ .

VERBAL PRACTICE

Talk about it

Discuss
Listen
Write

Discuss ideas with your partner, listen to classmates, and then write your favorite idea.

1. Many of my friends see me as (a/an) _____ _____

   person, but I **perceive** myself quite differently.

2. All the members of the _____ **perceived** one

   another as equals.

WRITING PRACTICE

Collaborate

Discuss
Agree
Write
Listen

Discuss ideas with your partner and agree on the best words to complete the frame. ▶

Sugar is often _____ as the leading cause of _____ .

Our Turn

Discuss
Listen
Write

Read the prompt. Work with the teacher to complete the frames. Write a thoughtful response that includes a convincing reason. ▶

PROMPT: Describe a problem that people usually perceive to be the effect of getting older. Then, provide an example of someone who is elderly that you perceive differently.

People usually _____ getting older to be the cause of _____

_____ . However, my _____ who is approximately

_____ years old, is actually quite _____ .

Be an Academic Author

Write
Discuss
Listen

Read the prompt and complete the frames. Strengthen your response with a convincing reason.

PROMPT: Describe a time when you perceived that someone was one way, such as shy, nerdy, or uncaring, but later you realized you were wrong. What changed?

In the past, I _____ my _____ to

be _____ . However, the way I _____ (him/her)

_____ changed after (he/she) _____ _____

_____ .

Construct a Response

Write
Discuss
Listen

Read the prompt and brainstorm ideas for a thoughtful response. Include a personal experience to strengthen your response.

PROMPT: Imagine that you are planning to do something outside, such as go hiking or play basketball. However, just as you are about to leave, a parent asks you to babysit a younger sibling or relative, and you become extremely angry. How can you change how you perceive the situation?

_____

_____

_____

grammar tip ▶

An **adverb** describes an action and can go before or after a verb. The adverbs *usually, often, shortly, confidently,* and *accurately* are examples of adverbs that can go before or after a verb.

EXAMPLE: My daughter **often** cooks eggs for breakfast. She **usually** scrambles them with cheese.

generalization
noun

 Write it: _____ **Write it again:** _____

 _____

TOOLKIT

Meaning a statement about something that is based on limited facts and which may be only partly true	**Examples** • The player's **generalization** that girls can't pitch very well inspired Mo'ne Davis to _____ him out.
Synonyms • conclusion	• A broad **generalization** about boys is that they are less _____ , but that is inaccurate.

Forms
• **Singular:** generalization
• **Plural:** generalizations

Family
• **Verb:** generalize

Word Partners
• broad generalization
• make a generalization

Examples
• It's a **broad generalization** to say that all college students are rich.
• When you know only a few people from a different country, it's hard not to **make a generalization** about their culture.

 Try It

If I had to make a **generalization** about the weather in this area, I would say it's

_____ .

VERBAL PRACTICE

Talk about it   Discuss ideas with your partner, listen to classmates, and then write your favorite idea.

Discuss
Listen
Write

1. A common **generalization** that people often make about athletes like _____

_____ players is that they are usually _____ .

2. I agree with the **generalization** that babies _____

_____ .

generalization

noun

Collaborate

Discuss
Agree
Write
Listen

Discuss ideas with your partner and agree on the best words to complete the frame. ▶

One _____ that you can make about our school is that the _____

_____ .

Our Turn

Discuss
Listen
Write

Read the prompt. Work with the teacher to complete the frames. Write a thoughtful response that includes a personal experience. ▶

PROMPT: Provide a broad generalization about Americans that you disagree with. Why do you disagree?

"All Americans are _____" is an example of a broad

_____ with which I disagree. From my perspective, most Americans I

know are actually _____ .

Be an Academic Author

Write
Discuss
Listen

Read the prompt and complete the frames. Strengthen your response with a convincing reason. ▶

PROMPT: Identify a famous person that many people make generalizations about. What do people typically say? Is this generalization accurate? Why or why not?

A famous person that many people make _____ about is _____

_____ . People typically say that

(he/she) _____ is very _____ . This seems to

be (accurate/inaccurate) _____ because (he/she) _____ often

_____ .

Construct a Response

Write
Discuss
Listen

Read the prompt and brainstorm ideas for a thoughtful response. Include a personal experience to strengthen your response. ▶

PROMPT: People often misjudge certain pet breeds based on limited or inaccurate information. Identify a breed that is misunderstood and dispel the broad generalization.

_____

_____

_____

---

grammar tip ▶

An **adjective** describes, or tells about, a noun. An adjective sometimes appears after verbs such as *is*, *are*, *look*, *feel*, *smell*, and *taste*.

EXAMPLE: I prefer to make pasta sauce with fresh vegetables and basil because it smells **delicious** and tastes **better** than a canned sauce.

perception

noun

Say it: per • **cep** • tion

Write it: _____   **Write it again:** _____

_____

Meaning
your belief or opinion about what someone or something is like

Synonyms
• belief, impression

Examples
• The reporter _____ several people so viewers could hear various **perceptions** of the event.

• My inaccurate **perception** of _____ changed after I saw several cute photos and learned about their role in the environment.

Forms
• **Singular:** perception
• **Plural:** perceptions

Family
• **Verb:** perceive
• **Adjectives:** perceptive, perceptible
• **Adverbs:** perceivably, perceptively

Word Partners
• a common/widespread perception
• accurate/inaccurate perception

Examples
• It is **a common perception** in this country that if you work hard, you can become rich.
• A group of Muslim students from our school are working in the community to change some people's **inaccurate perceptions** about them.

Try It

A common **perception** about electric cars is that they are _____
_____ .

Talk about it

Discuss
Listen
Write

Discuss ideas with your partner, listen to classmates, and then write your favorite idea.

1. In order to get an accurate **perception** of what _____ _____ is truly like, you need to experience it yourself or at least listen empathetically to many firsthand accounts.

2. In other countries, there is a widespread **perception** that the United States is a land of _____ .

Unit 7

perception

noun

Collaborate

Discuss
Agree
Write
Listen

Discuss ideas with your partner and agree on the best words to complete the frame. ▶

There is a common _____ that cats are _____ .

In reality, there are many personality _____ among cats.

Our Turn

Discuss
Listen
Write

Read the prompt. Work with the teacher to complete the frames. Write a thoughtful response that includes a convincing reason. ▶

PROMPT: **What is one inaccurate perception people sometimes have about you? Why do they think this way? How is their perception inaccurate?**

One inaccurate _____ people often have about me is that I am

_____ . They think this because _____ ,

_____ , but I actually _____

_____ .

Be an Academic Author

Write
Discuss
Listen

Read the prompt and complete the frames. Strengthen your response with a relevant example. ▶

PROMPT: **Think of a common negative perception adults have about teenagers. In your experience, is this perception accurate?**

A widespread negative _____ adults have about teenagers is that we

_____ . In my experience, this perception is

(accurate/inaccurate) _____ because _____

_____ .

Construct a Response

Write
Discuss
Listen

Read the prompt and brainstorm ideas for a thoughtful response. Construct a response that includes a relevant example and personal experience. ▶

PROMPT: **As we learn more about things, our perceptions evolve. Describe an inaccurate or distorted perception you had about something that changed as you came to know more about it.**

_____

_____

_____

grammar tip ▶

Singular nouns name one person, place, thing, or idea. The words *a, an, the*, and *one* often appear before a singular noun.

EXAMPLE: The piano **player** made an obvious **mistake** during the **performance**.

presume
verb

Say it: pre • **sume**

Write it: _____   **Write it again:** _____

_____

Meaning	Examples	
to think that something is probably true	• We **presumed** the _____ cat was hungry, so we offered it some food.	
Synonyms • believe; assume	• When the principal saw the boy in front of the fresh _____ , she automatically **presumed** that he had painted it.	

TOOLKIT

Forms
• **Present:**
  I/You/We/They   presume
  He/She/It   presumes
• **Past:**   presumed

Family
• **Noun:** presumption
• **Adjective:** presumptive
• **Adverb:** presumably

Word Partners
• correctly/wrongly presume that
• automatically presume that

Examples
• My vocabulary was so sophisticated that my teacher **wrongly presumed that** my paper was plagiarized.
• When my brother couldn't find his jacket, he **automatically presumed that** I was to blame because I had borrowed it once before.

 Try It

When my friend didn't eat his lunch, I correctly **presumed** that _____

_____ .

VERBAL PRACTICE

Talk about it   Discuss ideas with your partner, listen to classmates, and then write your favorite idea.

    Discuss
    Listen
    Write

1. If I arrived at school and saw crowds of students outside the building, I would automatically **presume** that _____ .

2. I **presumed** that I would lose the _____ , since there were dozens of participants, but I ended up winning second place.

presume
verb

WRITING PRACTICE

Collaborate

Discuss
Agree
Write
Listen

Discuss ideas with your partner and agree on the best words to complete the frame. ▶

When we first heard the crackle of the loudspeaker, we immediately _____ that

the principal was going to _____ .

Our Turn

Discuss
Listen
Write

Read the prompt. Work with the teacher to complete the frames. Write a thoughtful response that includes a personal experience. ▶
PROMPT: **Think of a time you saw someone buying a large quantity of something at the supermarket. What did you presume about the person?**

One time, the person in front of us in line at the supermarket was buying a lot of _____

_____ . I _____ that (he/she) _____

_____ .

Be an Academic Author

Write
Discuss
Listen

Read the prompt and complete the frames. Strengthen your response with a personal experience.
PROMPT: **What kinds of activities do people automatically presume you are interested in before they know you? What activities do you really like?**

Many people automatically _____ that because I am (a/an) _____ _____

_____ , I must be interested in _____ .

Personally, I prefer _____ .

Construct a Response

Write
Discuss
Listen

Read the prompt and brainstorm ideas for a thoughtful response. Construct a response that includes a personal experience and a convincing reason. ▶
PROMPT: **Have you ever made an incorrect presumption about someone based on a first impression? What did you wrongly presume, and why?**

_____

_____

_____

grammar tip ▶

A **past tense verb** describes an action that already happened. For verbs that end in silent *e*, drop the final *e* before you add *-ed*.

EXAMPLE: Our teacher **surprised** us when she **announced** that we were having a quiz.

conclusion

noun

 Write it: _____ **Write it again:** _____

 _____

TOOLKIT

Meaning	**Examples**
a decision that something is true, after thinking about it a lot	• When I saw fans _____ in the street, I drew the **conclusion** that Spain had won the World Cup. 
Synonyms • decision; judgment	• It is important for a jury to consider all the _____ before coming to a **conclusion** about a person's guilt or innocence. 

Forms
- **Singular:** conclusion
- **Plural:** conclusions

Family
- **Verb:** conclude
- **Adjective:** conclusive

Word Partners
- come to the conclusion that
- a (logical/reasonable/valid) conclusion

Examples
- After examining the half-eaten flowers and vegetables, my brother **came to the conclusion that** rabbits had broken into the garden.
- My mom said that the dent in the bumper was from someone hitting our car in the parking lot, which was **a reasonable conclusion**.

 Try It

After wasting an entire day on _____ , I've come to the **conclusion** that I should take a break from it for a while.

VERBAL PRACTICE

Talk about it

Discuss ideas with your partner, listen to classmates, and then write your favorite idea.

Discuss
Listen
Write

1. If my friend _____

_____ , I would come to the **conclusion** that she was angry with me.

2. If you suddenly get stuck in heavy traffic, but it's not rush hour, one valid **conclusion** you

might reach is that there is (a/an) _____ _____

_____ .

conclusion

noun

WRITING PRACTICE

Collaborate

Discuss
Agree
Write
Listen

Discuss ideas with your partner and agree on the best words to complete the frame. ▶

After reviewing the test data, the committee has come to the _____ that students

need more access to _____ .

Our Turn

Discuss
Listen
Write

Read the prompt. Work with the teacher to complete the frames. Write a thoughtful response
that includes a relevant example and a convincing reason.

PROMPT: Imagine you and a parent left the grocery store and couldn't find your car. What is one logical
conclusion you could reach about what has happened? Explain how you came to this conclusion.

If my parent and I left the grocery story and couldn't find our car, one logical _____

we could reach is that it was _____ . I might think

this because _____

_____ .

Be an Academic Author

Write
Discuss
Listen

Read the prompt and complete the frames. Strengthen your response with a relevant example.

PROMPT: Sometimes people draw different conclusions from the same data. What do some people
think about climate change, for example? What do you think? ▶

Many scientists agree that climate change _____

_____ . However, many people have looked at the same data and

drawn the _____ that it is not (a/an) _____ _____

problem. Personally, I think this issue is _____ because

_____ .

Construct a Response

Write
Discuss
Listen

Read the prompt and brainstorm ideas for a thoughtful response. Construct a response that
includes a personal experience.

PROMPT: People often experience the same situation differently. Think about an event that you and
a friend experienced together. What conclusions did you each draw about what you saw, and why?

_____

_____

_____

grammar tip ▶

The **present perfect tense** is formed with *has/have* + the **past participle** form of the verb.
To write the past participle of a regular verb, use the base form of the verb plus *-ed*. For verbs
that end in silent *e*, drop the final *e* before you add *-ed*.

EXAMPLE: My mother **has played** the piano for years. We **have enjoyed** hearing it.

expand

REVIEW: direct *adjective*

DAY 1

My bad mood was a _____ result of _____

_____ .

expand *verb*

DAY 2

I know that you didn't like the _____ that I recommended, but

could you please _____ on your reaction by sharing your reasons with me?

DAY 3

In order to _____ upon my knowledge about _____ ,

I spent some time reading online articles.

DAY 4

I raised my hand and correctly responded to the teacher's question in class about

_____ , and then she _____ on my

answer by providing more details.

DAY 5

A dictionary often _____ on the definition of a word by

_____ .

TOTAL

136

SMART START

DAY 1

REVIEW: expand *verb*

In order to convince your parents to allow you to participate in an activity that

_____ you

will need to _____ on the benefits and your heartfelt reasons

for wanting to do it.

perceive *verb*

DAY 2

We all _____ the world differently. For some, it's a

_____ place in which we must be careful and pay

attention to our surroundings. For others, it's a wonderful place full of amazing beauty.

DAY 3

I wonder whether bullies _____ themselves as bullies, or whether

they think they are just _____ .

DAY 4

Once you let (a/an) _____ _____ circulate, many people

will _____ it to be true, even if it's proven to be false.

DAY 5

My friend is extremely interesting, smart, and talented, but unfortunately she

_____ herself as _____ .

TOTAL

generalization

REVIEW: perceive   *verb*

DAY 1

Different people _____ flavors differently. For example,

many people can't stand _____ , but I enjoy it.

generalization   *noun*

DAY 2

Based on his first encounter with a neighbor's dog, the little boy made the

_____ that all dogs are _____ .

DAY 3

Broad _____ about a group of people can be unfair because they don't take

into account each person's _____ .

DAY 4

One _____ often made about cowboys in movies is that

they are _____ .

DAY 5

Your negative experience at one _____

does not justify your _____ that they are all bad.

TOTAL

SMART START

REVIEW: generalization *noun*

DAY 1

One _____ you could make about animated movies is that they

are usually _____ .

☐
☐

perception *noun*

DAY 2

Meeting more people from different _____ may

help you overcome your negative or inaccurate _____ of them.

☐
☐

DAY 3

As humans, our _____ can be wildly inaccurate. For example,

we may mistake the sound of the wind for a bird call or the shadow of a tree outside for

(a/an) _____ .

☐
☐

DAY 4

It's a common _____ among young children that vegetables

are _____ , but this usually changes as they get older.

☐
☐

DAY 5

Many middle schoolers share the _____ that

_____ is old-fashioned and unappealing.

☐
☐

TOTAL

presume

REVIEW: perception   *noun*

DAY 1

My friend had a negative _____ of _____

_____ , until I actually made her try some—and she loved it!

presume   *verb*

DAY 2

We _____ that it was acceptable to _____

_____ in the study area at the library, but the librarian immediately

came over and told us not to.

DAY 3

I was annoyed when the server at the restaurant mistakenly _____ that

I _____ .

DAY 4

When we saw the crow sitting on the ground and not moving, we initially

_____ that it was _____ , but

shortly it began to move and flew away.

DAY 5

When we saw how _____ the invitations to the party were, we

automatically _____ that we would need to get dressed up in our

best clothes.

TOTAL

 **SMART** START

REVIEW: presume *verb*

DAY 1

The old man always dressed in such _____ clothes, that many

people _____ that he was poor, but he was actually quite well off.

☐
☐

---

conclusion *noun*

DAY 2

If the board of health closes a local restaurant, one _____ I might

draw is that the restaurant _____

_____ .

☐
☐

DAY 3

If I saw a parrot in the tree behind my house, a logical _____

would be that _____ .

☐
☐

DAY 4

After reading the short story, some students reached different _____

about the main character's _____ .

☐
☐

DAY 5

If a normally reliable friend is more than 30 minutes late, a reasonable

_____ to draw is that _____

_____ .

☐
☐

TOTAL

Argument

To make an **argument** means to explain why you believe something is true by supporting it with convincing reasons, relevant examples, and personal experiences.

 Find It Read the sentences. Underline the best reason, example, or experience to support each argument.

1. Music programs should not be cut from school curriculum as they help students' academic performance.

   a. Studies show that learning music helps students develop language and reasoning skills, which helps them excel in subjects like math and English.
   b. Music is an outlet for expression, which can help students approach academic work more creatively.
   c. Being a part of a band or orchestra helps students learn how to work together as a team.

2. To reduce road accidents, there should be a national ban on the use of cell phones while driving.

   a. It is difficult for drivers to pay attention to other drivers when they are distracted by their phones.
   b. Road conditions can change very quickly.
   c. According to the FCC, in 2014, there were 3,179 fatalities involving drivers using cell phones.

 Try It Write one convincing reason to support the argument.

Homework should be limited to two hours a night. One important reason is that more homework causes students to _____ .

RATE WORD KNOWLEDGE

Rate how well you know Toolkit words you'll use when you prepare to argue.

6th Grade	7th Grade	RATE IT			
		BEFORE	8th Grade	AFTER	
claim	point	1 2 3 4	**crucial**	1 2 3 4	
proof	emphasis	1 2 3 4	**assert**	1 2 3 4	
state	justify	1 2 3 4	**opposition**	1 2 3 4	
emphasize	logical	1 2 3 4	**principle**	1 2 3 4	
support	relevance	1 2 3 4	**resolve**	1 2 3 4	
compelling	valid	1 2 3 4	**sufficient**	1 2 3 4	

DISCUSSION GUIDE
- Form groups of four.
- Assign letters to each person.
- Each group member takes a turn leading a discussion.
- Prepare to report about one word.

Ⓐ Ⓑ Ⓓ Ⓒ

DISCUSS WORDS

Discuss how well you know the eighth grade words. Then, report to the class how you rated each word.

 Ask

So, _____ what do you know
(NAME)

about the word _____ ?

 Discuss

1 = I **don't recognize** the word _____ .

I need to learn what it means.

2 = I **recognize** the word _____ ,

but I need to learn the meaning.

3 = I'm **familiar** with the word _____ .

I think it means _____ .

4 = I **know** the word _____ .

It's a _____ , and it means _____ .
(PART OF SPEECH)

Here is my example sentence: _____ .

 Report Word Knowledge

Our group gave the word _____ a rating of _____ because _____ .

SET A GOAL AND REFLECT

First, set a vocabulary goal for this unit by selecting at least three words that you plan to thoroughly learn. At the end of the unit, return to this page and write a reflection about one word you have mastered.

GOAL

During this unit I plan to thoroughly learn the words _____ ,

_____ , and _____ . Increasing my word knowledge will

help me speak and write effectively when I need to argue a point.

As a result of this unit, I feel most confident about the word _____ .

This is my model sentence: _____

_____ .

 **REFLECTION**

crucial
adjective

Say it: cru • cial

Write it: _____ **Write it again:** _____

_____

Meaning necessary, very important	**Examples** • It is **crucial** to let your doctor know if you are allergic to any kinds of _____ .
Synonyms • critical	• Finding a new _____ was **crucial** to the success of the baseball team.

Family
• **Adverb:** crucially

Word Partners
• crucial to the success of
• play a crucial role in

Examples
• Volunteers were **crucial to the success of** the food drive.
• The actor's agent **played a crucial role in** getting him a part in the play.

Try It
If you are travelling to _____ , it is **crucial** that you bring a warm coat.

VERBAL PRACTICE

Talk about it   Discuss ideas with your partner, listen to classmates, and then write your favorite idea.

Discuss
Listen
Write

1. In social studies, we learned how _____

   played a **crucial** role in American history.

2. Learning how to _____ plays a **crucial** role in your

   success in school.

144   Unit 8

WRITING PRACTICE

Collaborate
Discuss
Agree
Write
Listen

Discuss ideas with your partner and agree on the best words to complete the frame. ▶

One thing that is _____ to your success in playing (the/a/an) _____

_____ is to practice every day.

Our Turn
Discuss
Listen
Write

Read the prompt. Work with the teacher to complete the frames. Write a thoughtful response that includes a relevant example.
PROMPT: Think about a critical issue facing your school. What is the problem and what would you suggest as a solution?

One _____ issue facing our school is the _____

_____ . As a solution, I would suggest _____

_____ .

Be an Academic Author
Write
Discuss
Listen

Read the prompt and complete the frames. Strengthen your response with a relevant example.
PROMPT: Describe a device, such as a smartphone or computer, that plays a crucial role in your ability to communicate with your friends or family members. Why?

One device that plays a _____ role in my ability to communicate with my

_____ is my _____ . For example, I use it

to _____ about _____

_____ almost every day.

Construct a Response
Write
Discuss
Listen

Read the prompt and brainstorm ideas for a thoughtful response. Include a convincing reason to strengthen your response. ▶
PROMPT: What do you think about some proposals to raise the driving age to 18 instead of 16? Does being able to drive at age 16 play a crucial role in planning your near future? Why or why not?

_____

_____

_____

grammar tip ▶

Use a **verb + ing** after the prepositions *by, of, in,* and *for*.

EXAMPLE: Coach John demonstrated different techniques **for throwing** the discus and shot put.

assert
verb

 Write it: _____ **Write it again:** _____

 _____

<table>
<tr><td colspan="2">

Meaning

to say clearly or firmly that something is true, or that you believe you have certain rights

Synonyms

• declare; insist; maintain

</td><td>

Examples

• Our coach **asserts** that wearing _____ during all contact will protect players from injury.

• My cousin was suspended for littering, but he **asserts** that the garbage was not _____ .

</td><td>

</td></tr>
</table>

TOOLKIT

Forms
- **Present:**

  I/You/We/They   assert

  He/She/It   asserts
- **Past:**   asserted

Family
- **Noun:** assertion
- **Adjective:** assertive

Word Partners
- confidently/forcefully/ strongly assert
- assert (your/his/her) claim/ rights/independence

Examples
- The authors of the report **strongly asserted** that water quality is the most serious health problem across the globe.
- The team captain **asserted his right** to play in the championship game.

 Try It

I **asserted** repeatedly that I had not broken my brother's _____ , but he wouldn't believe me.

VERBAL PRACTICE

Talk about it   Discuss ideas with your partner, listen to classmates, and then write your favorite idea.

   Discuss
   Listen
   Write

1. The student council president **asserted** confidently that this year's Run for Funds drive would

   raise enough money to purchase _____

   for every classroom.

2. The substitute math teacher needs to **assert** his right to penalize disrespectful behavior when

   students start to _____ .

assert
verb

Collaborate

Discuss
Agree
Write
Listen

Discuss ideas with your partner and agree on the best words to complete the frame. ▶

My friends and I _____ that high schools in our area should find more

ways for students to _____ .

Our Turn

Discuss
Listen
Write

Read the prompt. Work with the teacher to complete the frames. Write a thoughtful response that includes a relevant example. ▶

PROMPT: Many parents assert that videogames are more harmful than beneficial for teens. What evidence would you use to counter their argument?

Although many parents _____ that videogames are harmful for teens,

I have a more positive _____ . In my experience, a videogame such

as _____ can actually teach valuable skills, including how to

_____ .

Be an Academic Author

Write
Discuss
Listen

Read the prompt and complete the frames. Strengthen your response with a relevant example. ▶

PROMPT: Some educators firmly believe that texting has negatively affected students' formal written communication. Offer evidence they might use to assert their claim.

To _____ their beliefs that texting has negatively affected students'

academic writing, educators should draw from their own _____

_____ . For example, they could point out that students now

regularly include _____ in their formal essays, such as

_____ and _____ .

Construct a Response

Write
Discuss
Listen

Read the prompt and brainstorm ideas for a thoughtful response. Include relevant examples to strengthen your response.

PROMPT: Describe a time you asserted yourself when you felt someone had treated you unfairly.

_____

_____

_____

grammar tip ▶

The **preposition** *to* needs to be followed by a verb in the base form.

EXAMPLE: I want *to* join a volleyball team this summer, but my parents think it would be better for me *to* find a part-time job.

opposition
noun

 Write it: _____   **Write it again:** _____

 _____

<table>
<tr><td colspan="2">

Meaning
strong disagreement
</td><td>

Examples
- The president was surprised by the **opposition** to his proposed _____ increase.
</td><td rowspan="2">
</td></tr>
<tr><td colspan="2">

Synonyms
- disagreement; protest
</td><td>

- The developer's plan to cut down trees to build a _____ course met with strong **opposition**.
</td></tr>
</table>

TOOLKIT

Forms
- **Singular:** opposition
- **Plural:** opposition

Family
- **Verb:** oppose
- **Adjectives:** opposing, opposed, opposite

Word Partners
- express (my/your/his/her/our/their) opposition
- strong/tremendous opposition

Examples
- The groups **expressed their opposition** to the capture of dolphins.
- There is **strong opposition** in my neighborhood to the plan to build a car wash.

 Try It
I would face **opposition** at home if I tried to _____ .

VERBAL PRACTICE

Talk about it

Discuss
Listen
Write

Discuss ideas with your partner, listen to classmates, and then write your favorite idea.

1. If our teacher assigned us (a/an) _____ _____

   _____ over the break, there would be tremendous **opposition** from

   students.

2. Animal rights activists expressed their strong **opposition** to having _____

   _____ in amusement parks.

WRITING PRACTICE

Collaborate

Discuss
Agree
Write
Listen

Discuss ideas with your partner and agree on the best words to complete the frame. ▶

Many nations joined together to express their tremendous _____ to the

increasing use of _____ .

Our Turn

Discuss
Listen
Write

Read the prompt. Work with the teacher to complete the frames. Write a thoughtful response that includes a personal experience. ▶

PROMPT: **Describe a time when you felt a strong opposition to certain activities that a friend wanted to do during the weekend. What did you do?**

One weekend, my friend wanted to _____

_____ , but I felt a strong _____ because it would be

_____ . As a result, I encouraged (him/her) _____ to

_____ instead.

Be an Academic Author

Write
Discuss
Listen

Read the prompt and complete the frames. Strengthen your response with a convincing reason.

PROMPT: **Identify a particularly productive way for students to express their opposition to an unpopular school policy.** ▶

If students disagree with a school policy, there are some ways to express their

_____ that are more productive than others. For example, rather

than simply _____ to classmates, students can

_____ to change the policy.

Construct a Response

Write
Discuss
Listen

Read the prompt and brainstorm ideas for a thoughtful response. Include a convincing reason to strengthen your response. ▶

PROMPT: **Many family physicians support a tax on soda purchases as a means of reducing child obesity. What opposition might a soda tax face from your community members?**

_____

_____

_____

grammar tip ▶

An **adjective** describes, or tells about, a noun. Usually an adjective goes before the noun it describes. Adjectives are always singular even if they describe a plural noun.

EXAMPLE: My sister is an extremely **talented** painter. Her portraits always have **beautiful** shading and she uses **rich** colors.

principle

noun

 Write it: _____   **Write it again:** _____

 _____

TOOLKIT

Meaning a basic rule or idea about what is right	**Examples** • One of our school's basic **principles** is _____ for every student.

Synonyms • rule, belief	• As a matter of **principle**, our cafeteria doesn't serve any sugary _____ .

Forms
- **Singular:** principle
- **Plural:** principles

Family
- **Adjective:** principled

Word Partners
- basic principle

- a matter of principle

Examples
- Two of the **basic principles** of being a good parent are establishing rules and setting limits.
- As **a matter of principle**, I would never join a club if my friends weren't allowed to join as well.

 Try It

I refuse to wear _____ as a matter of **principle**.

VERBAL PRACTICE

Talk about it

Discuss
Listen
Write

Discuss ideas with your partner, listen to classmates, and then write your favorite idea.

1. One of the basic **principles** of being a good friend is _____ .

2. It is against my **principles** to _____ .

WRITING PRACTICE

Collaborate
Discuss
Agree
Write
Listen

Discuss ideas with your partner and agree on the best words to complete the frame. ▶

It isn't always easy to stick to your _____ because there could be situations

where you might _____ .

Our Turn
Discuss
Listen
Write

Read the prompt. Work with the teacher to complete the frames. Write a thoughtful response that includes a valid reason.
PROMPT: **Identify a particular job, such as being a doctor or judge, and the strong principles that are crucial to success in this career.**

If you want to have a job as (a/an) _____ _____ , it is important to have

strong _____ . In particular, you must be very _____ because it

is crucial to success when working with _____ .

Be an Academic Author
Write
Discuss
Listen

Read the prompt and complete the frames. Strengthen your response with relevant example. ▶
PROMPT: **Describe two of the basic principles that every good coach should remember.**

Two basic _____ that every good coach should remember are that

_____ , and to

be _____ when assisting atheletes. For example, a competitor

could be struggling with a new _____ , so the coach should take his or her

time to _____ .

Construct a Response
Write
Discuss
Listen

Read the prompt and brainstorm ideas for a thoughtful response. Include a convincing reason to strengthen your response.
PROMPT: **Describe two or more strong principles that a teacher must possess. Why are they important?**

_____

_____

_____

grammar tip ▶

Use the **modal verb**, or helping verb, *could* to show that something might be possible. When you use *could*, add a verb in the base form.

EXAMPLE: My sister **could** eat nachos everyday. However, she **could** also gain weight.

resolve
verb

Say it: re • solve

 Write it: _____   **Write it again:** _____

 _____

Meaning
to find a solution to a problem or argument; or to decide to do something

Synonyms
- solve, fix, settle
- decide; determine

Examples
- Mrs. Watkins quickly **resolved** the argument about who would sit in the _____ seat.

- Nina **resolved** to start _____ on New Year's Day.

Forms
- **Present:**

  I/You/We/They   resolve

  He/She/It   resolves
- **Past:**   resolved

Family
- **Adjective:** resolute, resolved
- **Adverb:** resolutely

Word Partners
- resolve (the/an) argument/issue/problem/conflict
- attempt to/strive to/try to resolve

Examples
- The Thirteenth Amendment **resolved the issue** of slavery for all.
- Before you can **attempt to resolve** a problem, you must understand what it is.

 Try It
After receiving a disappointing grade on a test, serious students **resolve** to _____ more frequently.

VERBAL PRACTICE

Talk about it   Discuss ideas with your partner, listen to classmates, and then write your favorite idea.

Discuss
Listen
Write

1. This week, I have **resolved** to _____

   _____ when I get home each day.

2. You will never **resolve** an argument by _____ .

resolve
verb

WRITING PRACTICE

Collaborate

Discuss
Agree
Write
Listen

Discuss ideas with your partner and agree on the best words to complete the frame. ▶

Some people productively _____ issues with family members and friends by

_____ , while others prefer to hold grudges.

Our Turn

Discuss
Listen
Write

Read the prompt. Work with the teacher to complete the frames. Write a thoughtful response that includes a relevant example. ▶

PROMPT: **A newly-elected president usually attempts to resolve many urgent national problems. What national issue should our president strive to resolve immediately?**

One national issue that our president should strive to _____ is the probem of

_____ . For example, this issue negatively impacts my community

by _____

_____ .

Be an Academic Author

Write
Discuss
Listen

Read the prompt and complete the frames. Strengthen your response with a relevant example.

PROMPT: **Describe an issue that seems to be of particular importance for teachers at your school. Why do you think it is so important for them to attempt to resolve this issue?**

The issue of _____ seems

to be of particular importance to the teachers at our school. One reason that I think

it is so important for them to attempt to _____ this issue is because it

_____ .

Construct a Response

Write
Discuss
Listen

Read the prompt and brainstorm ideas for a thoughtful response. Include a personal experience to strengthen your response. ▶

PROMPT: **When collaborating on a project, some team members can have differing opinions about process, responsibilities, and content. How can a team leader productively resolve arguments?**

_____

_____

_____

grammar tip ▶

Quantity adjectives tell "how much" or "how many." Quantity adjectives go before a plural noun. Common quantity adjectives are: *most, many, some, several, both.*

EXAMPLE: Most parks and **many** swimming pools were closed today for maintenance.

sufficient
adjective

Say it: suf • **fi** • cient

Write it: _____   **Write it again:** _____

_____

TOOLKIT

Meaning
enough of something

Synonyms
• enough

Antonyms
• insufficient

Examples
• When hiking on a hot day, make sure you bring **sufficient** _____ .

• Jose won the _____ because he provided **sufficient** evidence to prove his claim.

Family
• **Nouns:** sufficiency
• **Verb:** suffice
• **Adverb:** sufficiently

Word Partners
• sufficient evidence

• provide sufficient

Examples
• The principal had **sufficient evidence** to suspend the students for vandalism.
• Our teacher **provided sufficient** time for us to write our reports.

 Try It
Student collaborators must factor in **sufficient** time to carefully _____ their final draft.

VERBAL PRACTICE

Talk about it   Discuss ideas with your partner, listen to classmates, and then write your favorite idea.

Discuss
Listen
Write

1. _____ isn't a **sufficient** excuse

   for being late.

2. I think twenty minutes is **sufficient** time to take (a/an) _____ _____

   _____ quiz.

sufficient
adjective

Collaborate

Discuss
Agree
Write
Listen

Discuss ideas with your partner and agree on the best words to complete the frame. ▶

To convince the principal to permit _____ during final

exams, the student leadership team compiled _____ evidence highlighting

the positive effects.

Our Turn

Discuss
Listen
Write

Read the prompt. Work with the teacher to complete the frames. Write a thoughtful response that includes a personal experience and a relevant example. ▶

PROMPT: **Describe a class or activity that your school might offer if students show sufficient interest. How would this enhance student experiences?**

If students provide _____ interest, the school might offer (a/an) _____

_____ . This would enhance student experiences by

allowing us to _____ .

Be an Academic Author

Write
Discuss
Listen

Read the prompt and complete the frames. Strengthen your response with relevant examples. ▶

PROMPT: **Describe something that many underfunded communities lack sufficient resources to improve. If they were improved how would it impact the residents?**

Many underfunded communities lack _____ resources to improve their

_____ . However, if they were improved, the residents would be able

to _____ .

Construct a Response

Write
Discuss
Listen

Read the prompt and brainstorm ideas for a thoughtful response. Include convincing reasons to strengthen your response. ▶

PROMPT: **Although many teachers have strict assignment due dates, most would accept late work under special circumstances. Provide two sufficient reasons for receiving a three-day extension for a major U.S. history research report.**

_____

_____

_____

grammar tip ▶

Adjectives are always singular even if they describe a plural noun. Do not add **-s** to adjectives that describe plural nouns.

EXAMPLE: My neighbor is an **amazing** yoga instructor. She always performs **difficult** poses.

crucial

REVIEW: **conclusion**   *noun*

DAY 1

My friend came to the _____ that she was allergic

to _____ after having physical reactions to (it/them)

_____ several times.

☐

☐

crucial   *adjective*

DAY 2

A _____ plays a

_____ role in leading a happy life.

☐

☐

DAY 3

Strong leadership skills are _____ to the success of _____

_____ .

☐

☐

DAY 4

It's absolutely _____ to _____

if there is a fire in the building.

☐

☐

DAY 5

When taking a standardized test at school, it's _____ that you

_____ .

☐

☐

TOTAL

156

SMART START

DAY 1

REVIEW: crucial   *adjective*

In order to get a high grade on your report, it's _____ that you

_____ .

☐

☐

assert   *verb*

DAY 2

My aunt has always _____ that having pets in the house is

_____ .

☐

☐

DAY 3

Even though it's very unlikely, the hiker still _____ that he saw

_____ in the woods, although his

companions claim otherwise.

☐

☐

DAY 4

In the environmental article, the author _____ the position that

_____ needed more government

protection.

☐

☐

DAY 5

After her rich great-aunt died, my friend's mother and aunts all tried to _____

their claims to her _____ .

☐

☐

TOTAL

opposition

 **SMART** *START*

REVIEW: assert *verb*

DAY 1

My grandmother looked rather _____ after her operation, but

the doctors _____ that she would be fine and able to go home in a

few days.

---

opposition *noun*

DAY 2

I would be in _____ to a proposal to remove _____

from the school lunch menu.

DAY 3

A large group of college students marched in the street to voice their _____

to _____ .

DAY 4

If my parents announced a plan to _____

_____ , they would face strong _____ from me.

DAY 5

The town's plan to put (a/an) _____ _____

in our community met with fierce _____ .

TOTAL

⚑ SMART START

REVIEW: opposition *noun*

DAY 1
Students at my school would be in strong _____ to a proposal to
_____ .

☐
☐

principle *noun*

DAY 2
It would be absolutely against my _____ to
_____ .

☐
☐

DAY 3
One of the basic _____ enshrined in the Bill of Rights in the

U.S. Constitution is the freedom of _____ .

☐
☐

DAY 4
One student's pushy parents tried to convince my teacher to

_____ ,

but she refused as a matter of _____ .

☐
☐

DAY 5
A hypocrite is someone who talks loudly about their high _____

but in reality _____ .

☐
☐

TOTAL

resolve

REVIEW: principle *noun*

DAY 1

Volunteering at a nursing home would be in line with the basic _____

of _____ .

☐
☐

resolve *verb*

DAY 2

We recently _____ the problem we were having with our Internet

connection by _____ .

☐
☐

DAY 3

A tech-savvy student helped the teacher to _____ an issue she was

having with the _____ .

☐
☐

DAY 4

When the two brothers couldn't agree on which show to watch on TV,

their mother _____ the heated dispute by

_____ .

☐
☐

DAY 5

Despite feeling lazy yesterday, my friend and I _____ to be productive

and _____ .

☐
☐

TOTAL

SMART START

REVIEW: resolve *verb*

DAY 1

A good _____ excels at _____ conflicts

between opposing groups of people.

☐

☐

sufficient *adjective*

DAY 2

Five dollars is a _____ amount of money to buy

_____ .

☐

☐

DAY 3

The _____ provided police

with _____ evidence to prove that their suspect committed

the crime.

☐

☐

DAY 4

I (think/don't think) _____ the school provides students with

_____ time for lunch. I believe that _____ is

the perfect amount of time.

☐

☐

DAY 5

Scientific studies did not produce _____ data to demonstrate that

the new medication was _____ .

☐

☐

TOTAL

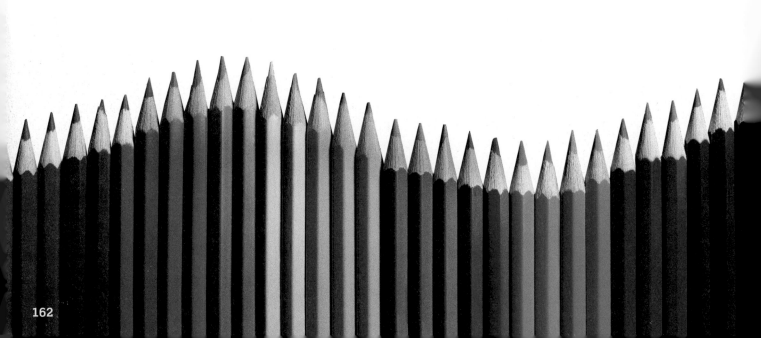

▶ grammar lessons

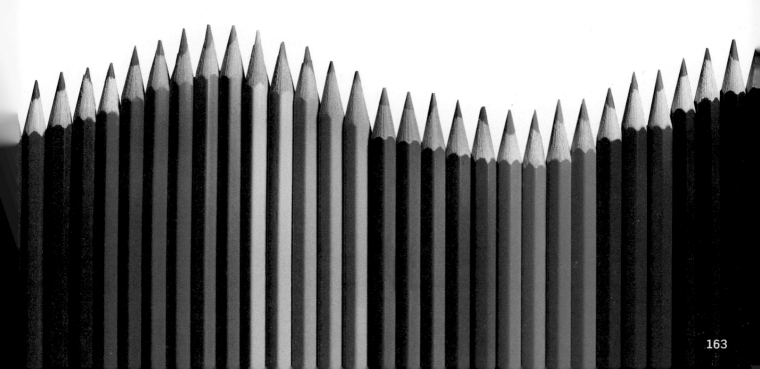

grammar

▶ **Present Tense Verbs**

Use the **present tense** when you talk about actions that happen usually, sometimes, or regularly.

	Subject	Verb
Use the **base form** of the verb when the subject is *I, you, we,* or *they.*	I You We They	**need** more sleep. base form
Use the **-s** form of the verb when the subject is *he, she,* or *it.*	He She It	**needs** more sleep. -s form

- When the base form of the verb ends in *s, sh, ch,* or *x,* add **-es:**
  miss ⟶ *misses; wash* ⟶ *washes; catch* ⟶ *catches; fix* ⟶ *fixes*
- When the base form of the verb ends in a consonant + *y,* change the *y* to *i* and add **-es:** *cry* ⟶ *cries*

Find It

Read the sentences. Write the correct form of the present tense verb.

1. Recycling (reduce/reduces) _____ waste.

2. I (let/lets) _____ my parents know when I plan to meet a friend after school.

3. They (spend/spends) _____ too much time on social media.

4. Our textbook (illustrate/illustrates) _____ many concepts with graphs.

Try It

Complete the sentences using the correct form of the verb.

1. Sound (travel) _____ faster in water than in air.

2. I (use) _____ a planner to keep track of my assignments.

3. That type of bird (fly) _____ south for the winter.

4. We (review) _____ our notes after each class.

Discuss and Write

Collaborate

Discuss
Agree
Write
Listen

Work with a partner. Use the correct form of the verbs to complete the sentences.

1. place/
analyze

Our teacher often _____ us in pairs when we

_____ articles.

2. bother/
leave

It _____ my parents when I

_____ the lights on in my room.

3. wash/dry

After dinner each night, one person in my family _____

the dishes and another one _____ them.

4. make/find

When you _____ a claim, you must

_____ evidence in the text to support it.

Your Turn

Think
Write

Work independently. Use the correct form of the verbs and your own words to complete the sentences.

1. jump/try

Every morning my cat _____ on

my bed and _____ to wake me by

_____ .

2. make/
come

I _____ myself (a/an)

_____ after I _____

home from school each day.

3. ask/
discuss

Each Friday, my social studies teacher _____

questions about social issues such as _____ and

we _____ them.

grammar
▶ **Adjectives and Adverbs**

An *adjective* describes a noun.   An *adverb* describes a verb.

Adjective	Adverb
That is the **correct** answer.	They answered the question **correctly**.
The president gave a **brief** speech.	The president spoke **briefly**.
You are **punctual**.	You always arrive **punctually**.

- An adjective usually comes before the noun it describes. An adjective can also come directly after the verb *be*: New York City is big.
- An adverb usually comes after the verb it describes. Most adverbs are formed by adding *-ly* to an adjective: *careful* ⟶ *carefully*

🔍 Find It

Complete the sentences with either the adjective or the adverb.

1. We check the school calendar (regular/regularly) _____ to make sure we don't miss any important events.

2. The author read a (fascinating/fascinatingly) _____ excerpt from her book.

3. My brother is waiting (anxious/anxiously) _____ to find out if he got into the college he wants to go to.

4. The novel tells the story of the main character's (mysterious/mysteriously) _____ disappearance.

✏️ Try It

Complete the sentences using the correct form (adjective or adverb) of the word.

1. After eating a lot of chocolate, I slept (restless) _____ .

2. At first I thought he was (shy) _____ , but after we spoke for just a few minutes, he became very outgoing.

3. The audience applauded (wild) _____ at the end of the performance.

4. When she asked for help, we volunteered (immediate) _____ .

Discuss and Write

Collaborate

Discuss
Agree
Write
Listen

Work with a partner. Write the sentence, including the adverb or adjective provided.

1. (unrealistic)   The candidate made many promises.

_____

_____

2. (honest)   We asked the class for an assessment of our project.

_____

_____

3. (enthusiastically)   We cheered whenever our school's soccer team scored a goal.

_____

_____

Your Turn

Think
Write

Work independently. Use the correct form of the word (adjective or adverb) and your own words to complete the sentences.

1. (careful)   The students listened _____ as the teacher told

them the date of the _____ exam.

2. (important)   It's _____ to support your claim with

_____ from the article.

3. (strange)   I had a _____ dream that I was being chased by

(a/an) _____ .

4. (casual)   You can dress _____ when you go to (a/an)

_____ .

grammar

▶ **Adverbs of Frequency**

Use **adverbs of frequency** to talk about how often actions happen.

	Adverbs of Frequency	Examples with the Verb *Be*	Examples with Other Verbs
100%	**always**	I **am always** nervous before a test.	I **always feel** nervous before a test.
	usually	That TV show **is usually** enjoyable.	I **usually enjoy** watching it.
	often	She **is often** sick in the winter.	She **often catches** colds in the winter.
	sometimes	The train **is sometimes** late.	The train **sometimes arrives** late.
	rarely	The baby **is rarely** quiet.	The baby **rarely sits** quietly.
0%	**never**	We **are never** home on Saturday morning.	We **never stay** home on Saturday morning.

- Put adverbs of frequency after the verb *be*.
- Put adverbs of frequency before all other verbs.

Find It

Read the pairs of sentences. Underline the sentence that has the adverb of frequency in the right place.

1. Teenagers often take selfies. | Teenagers take often selfies.

2. That author's books are interesting usually. | That author's books are usually interesting.

3. I am tired always after lunch. | I am always tired after lunch.

4. People often misspell the word *independence*. | People misspell often the word *independence*.

Try It

Write the sentences and include the adverb of frequency. Be sure to put it in the correct place.

1. (rarely) We are talkative in the morning.

   _____

2. (always) I use a highlighter to mark important information in texts.

   _____

3. (never) My little brother does what he is told to do.

   _____

4. (usually) Cats and dogs don't get along.

   _____

Discuss and Write

Collaborate

Discuss
Agree
Write
Listen

Work with a partner. Complete the sentences using appropriate adverbs of frequency and your own words.

1. She _____ puts her assignments in a special

   _____ so that they never get misplaced.

2. People _____ send each other letters anymore. Instead,

   they mostly communicate through _____ .

3. We _____ study late at night because we know we

   wouldn't be able to _____ .

4. We _____ review our notes after class to make sure they

   are _____ .

Your Turn

Think
Write

Work independently. Complete the sentences using appropriate adverbs of frequency and your own words.

1. I _____ wish that my _____ was

   different, but I'm generally happy with it the way it is.

2. I feel strongly about my position on _____ and

   will _____ change my mind about it.

3. When I start to get sick, I _____ take some

   _____ because it always makes me feel better.

4. Consuming too much sugar _____ leads to problems such as

   _____ .

grammar

▶ **Present Progressive Tense**

Use the **present progressive** to talk about an action that is happening right now.

Subject	be	Verb + -ing
I	am	
He She It	is	listen**ing** carefully.
You We They	are	

- To form the progressive tense of most verbs, and **-ing** to the base form of the verb: read ⟶ **reading**
- For verbs that end in a consonant + **-e**, drop the **-e** before adding **-ing**: dance ⟶ **dancing**

Find It

Complete the sentences using the correct form of the verb.

1. The storm clouds are (gather) _____; It will rain soon.

2. I'm (try) _____ to figure out the meaning of the word based on its context.

3. Global warming is (cause) _____ many animals to become endangered.

4. The country's unemployment rates are (decline) _____ because the economy is improving.

Try It

Read the present tense sentences. Write the sentences as present progressive sentences.

1. The two candidates debate their ideas.
   _____

2. I try to figure out this math problem without help, but it's very difficult.
   _____

3. You spend too much time on your device.
   _____

4. I read the chapter again to make sure I understand it.
   _____

grammar

Discuss and Write

Collaborate

Discuss
Agree
Write
Listen

Work with a partner. Use the correct form of the verbs to complete the sentences.

1. hide/look   My little sister is _____ and her

friend is _____ for her.

2. rain/shine   The forecast says it is _____ , but

actually the sun is _____ .

3. ring/
answer   We are _____ the bell, but no one

is _____ .

Your Turn

Think
Write

Work independently. Use the correct form of the verb and your own words to complete the sentences.

1. examine   We are _____ the _____

under a microscope.

2. pollute   Humans are _____ the ocean with many

_____ .

3. move   The line to get tickets for the concert is _____ quite

_____ .

4. meet   My math teacher and my parents are _____ right

now to discuss my _____ .

grammar

▶ **Past Tense Verbs**

Use the **past tense** to talk about events or actions that have already happened.

Subject	Base Form of Verb + *-ed/-d*	
I He She It You We They	borrow**ed**	the book.

- To form the simple past tense of most regular verbs, add **-ed** to the base form of the verb: *listen* ⟶ *listened*
- For regular verbs that end in **-e**, add **-d**: *smile* ⟶ *smiled*

Find It

Read the sentences. Write the correct form of the verb.

1. My sister and I (share / shared) _____ a room until we moved to our new house.

2. I always (cite/cited) _____ several sources in my essays.

3. Our teacher last year always (asks/asked) _____ us to be precise with our descriptions.

4. World War II (end/ended) _____ in 1945.

Try It

Complete the sentences using the correct form of the verb.

1. She (respond) _____ to the ringing of her alarm clock yesterday morning by going back to sleep.

2. I (create) _____ an outline for my essay before I started writing it.

3. It was very helpful when my math teacher (demonstrate) _____ how to solve equations with exponents.

4. During the flight, I (order) _____ chicken, but I got beef.

Discuss and Write

Collaborate

Discuss
Agree
Write
Listen

Work with a partner. Use the correct form of the verbs to complete the sentences.

1. gasp/
guess

Last night, the audience _____ when the

magician _____ the right card.

2. embarrass/
call

His mother _____ him when she

_____ him sweetie pie in front of his friends.

3. decide/
gather

When we wrote our essay, first we _____ on

the claim we wanted to make, then we _____

evidence to support the claim.

4. return/
review

After our math teacher _____ our tests,

we _____ the questions that we answered

incorrectly.

Your Turn

Think
Write

**Work independently. Use the correct form of the verbs and your own words to complete the
sentences.**

1. apologize/
realize

I _____ when I _____

I had accidentally used his _____ .

2. watch/
explain

In science class today we _____ a

video that _____ the concept of

_____ .

3. boil/taste

After we _____ the broccoli,

it _____ really

_____ .

grammar
▶ **Possessive Nouns**

Use **possessive nouns** to show that something belongs to someone or something.

	Singular Noun	Possessive Noun	Example
To show that something belongs to someone or something, add an apostrophe (') and **-s** at the end of a singular noun.	phone	phone**'s**	The phone**'s** battery is dead.

	Plural Noun that ends in -s	Possessive Noun	Example
To show that something belongs to more than one person or thing, add an apostrophe (') at the end of a plural noun, following the –s.	phones	phones**'**	Both of the phone**s'** batteries are dead.

Find It

Complete the sentences using the correct possessive noun.

1. The (cartoon's/cartoons') _____ caption is clever.

2. All of the (address's/address') _____ zip codes are incorrect.

3. I can't get that (TV show's/TV shows') _____ theme song out of my head.

4. The (boy scout's/boy scouts') _____ badges covered their vests.

Try It

Complete the sentences with the correct possessive form of the noun.

1. You can find that (student) _____ phone number in the school directory.

2. Some of the (campers) _____ name tags are missing.

3. All of the (jackets) _____ zippers are broken.

4. The (sign) _____ lettering is so faded, I can't read it.

grammar
▶ **Possessive Nouns**

Discuss and Write

Collaborate **Work with a partner. Read the first sentence. Then complete the second sentence with the correct**
Discuss **possessive noun.**
Agree
Write
Listen **1.** The basement of the building is flooded.

The _____ basement is flooded.

2. The prices of those stores are comparable.

Those _____ prices are comparable.

3. The numbers in the charts are incorrect.

The _____ numbers are incorrect.

4. The decisions of the president impact the economy.

The _____ decisions impact the economy.

Your Turn **Work independently. Complete the sentences with the correct possessive form of the noun and**
Think **your own words.**
Write
1. (article)   I always mark an _____ key passages with a

_____ .

2. (twins)   The _____ faces are almost exactly alike;

however, only one of them has a _____ on his

nose.

3. (forecaster)   The _____ prediction about the storm was

_____ .

4. (shirts)   In my opinion, his numerous _____ patterns

are usually too _____ .

Possessive Nouns   **175**

grammar

▶ There, Their, They're

There, **their**, and **they're** are homophones. Homophones are words that have the same sound, but are spelled differently and have different meanings.

Word	Explanation	Example
there	*There* is an adverb that means *that place*. *There* is also used with the verb *be* to introduce a sentence or clause.	I can swim from here all the way to **there**. **There** are 206 bones in the adult human body.
their	*Their* shows ownership. It is always followed by a noun.	The tourists took hundreds of photos with **their** phones.
they're	*They're* is a contraction formed by putting together the words *they + are*.	**They're** both good teachers.

🔍 Find It

Read the sentences. Choose the correct word to complete the sentences.

1. (Their/They're) _____ the two best players in the baseball league.

2. Hens sit on (their/they're) _____ eggs to help them hatch.

3. We go (there/their) _____ often because it's close to our house.

4. I'm sure they will keep (there/their) _____ promise.

✏️ Try It

Complete the sentences using *there*, *their*, or *they're*.

1. On Memorial Day, we honor soldiers for _____ sacrifices.

2. We need this translated into French, but _____ are no French-speakers

in the class.

3. Chimpanzees grunt when _____ angry.

4. The new parents named _____ daughter Ayesha.

Discuss and Write

Collaborate

Discuss
Agree
Write
Listen

Work with a partner. Complete the sentences using *there*, *their*, and *they're*.

1. Don't you see the textbooks? _____ right over

_____ !

2. We knocked, but _____ was nobody

_____ .

3. _____ aren't enough sources cited in

_____ project.

Your Turn

Think
Write

Work independently. Complete the sentences with *there*, *their*, and *they're* and your own words.

1. I like the themes in the essays we're reading. _____ all very

_____ .

2. The twins asked _____ mother for permission to

_____ .

3. _____ are many different ways to relax when you are feeling

stress. For example, you can _____ .

4. Some dog owners train _____ dogs to

_____ .

grammar
▶ Modal Verbs

A **modal verb** is a helping verb that adds more meaning to the main verb.

Example Sentence	Subject	Modal	Base Form of Verb		Meaning
I **could** meet you on Monday or Friday this week.	I	could	meet	you on Monday or Friday this week.	Use *could* to show that something might be possible.
You **should** check your essay for spelling errors.	You	should	check	your essay for spelling errors.	Use *should* to make suggestions or recommendations.
I **would** come with you, but I have a lot of homework.	I	would	come	with you, but I have a lot of homework.	Use *would* to show that something is possible under certain conditions.

🔍 Find It

Read the sentences. Complete the sentences with the best modal choice.

1. My sister and I (would/could) _____ meet you at 9:00 A.M. tomorrow. We don't have any plans in the morning.

2. I think we (should/would) _____ forgive her for not helping with the project more, and give her a second chance.

3. I have a bad cold. If I didn't have a test today, I (could/would) _____ stay home.

4. Our teacher says we (would/should) _____ format our sources correctly, or our essay will be returned.

✏️ Try It

Complete the sentences with the correct modal + verb forms.

1. Depending on the context, the word "change" (could mean/would mean) _____ coins or *transform*.

2. If you want to make new friends, you (would join/should join) _____ some after school activities.

3. I (should make/would make) _____ us mac and cheese, but we don't have any milk.

Discuss and Write

Collaborate

Discuss
Agree
Write
Listen

Work with a partner. Complete the sentences with the best modal choices. Use the modals *could*, *should*, and *would*.

1. We _____ go to the beach tomorrow, but we

   _____ probably work on our presentation instead.

2. Our class _____ enter the math competition. I think we

   _____ probably win.

3. We _____ give him some good advice on how to prepare for

   middle school, but I don't think he _____ listen.

4. We _____ tell you the secret if we

   _____ , but we promised not to tell anyone.

Your Turn

Think
Write

Work independently. Choose the best modal and your own words to complete the sentences. Use the modals *could*, *should*, and *would*.

1. Each paragraph of your essay _____ have (a/an) _____

   _____ topic sentence.

2. If I got lost while I was in the city, I _____ probably

   _____ .

3. You _____ create computer passwords that are very

   _____ so that they cannot be guessed.

4. If I saw someone being bullied on social media, I _____

   definitely try to _____ .

Acknowledgments, continued from page ii

vi (tl) Leonardo Patrizi/ E+/Getty Images. (cr) Ververidis Vasilis/Shutterstock.com. (cl) Rawpixel.com/Shutterstock.com. (br) Thor Jorgen Udvang/Shutterstock.com. viii (tl) Billion Photos/Shutterstock.com. (cr) Antoniodiaz/Shutterstock.com. (cl) eldar nurkovic/Shutterstock.com. (br) Jacek Chabraszewski/Shutterstock.com. x (tl) Monkey Business Images/Shutterstock.com. (cr) Max Topchii/Shutterstock.com. (cl) untitled/Shutterstock.com. (br) Tetra Images/Tetra images/Getty Images. 2 ERproductions Ltd/Blend Images/Getty Images. 4 (tr1) Comaniciu Dan/Shutterstock.com. (tr2) Hideo Kurihara/Alamy Stock Photo. 6 (tr1) Railway fx/Shutterstock.com. (tr2) Cal Sport Media/Alamy Stock Photo. 8 (tr1) JPC-PROD/Shutterstock.com. (tr2) Valentin_Manolov/iStock/Getty Images. 10 (tr1) Sashkin/Shutterstock.com. (tr2) Sebastian Kaulitzki/Shutterstock.com. 12 (tr1) Pepsco Studio/Shutterstock.com. (tr2) Bokan/Shutterstock.com. 14 (tr1) Mlenny/E+/Getty Images. (tr2) StockLite/Shutterstock.com. 22 (tc) Nejron Photo/Shutterstock.com. (tr) Zack Frank/Shutterstock.com. 24 (tr1) Blend Images/Superstock. (tr2) Robyn Mackenzie/Shutterstock.com. 26 (tr1) Yakoniva/Alamy Stock Photo. (tr2) Matthew Chattle/Alamy Stock Photo. 28 (tr1) Steve Maslowski/Science Source/Getty Images. (tr2) Dragon Images/Shutterstock.com. 30 (tr1) Weerasak saeku/Shutterstock.com. (tr2) Emmanuel Dunand/AFP/Getty Images. 32 (tr1) AP Images/Marcio Jose Sanchez. (tr2) Guy J. Sagi/Shutterstock.com. 34 (tr1) Buyenlarge/Archive Photos/Getty Images. (tr2) PureStock/Alamy Stock Photo. 42 Monkey Business Images/Shutterstock.com. 44 (tr1)

Leonardo Patrizi/E+/Getty Images. (tr2) rez-art/iStock/Getty Images. 46 (tr1) Horsemen/Shutterstock.com. (tr2) Ververidis Vasilis/Shutterstock.com. 48 (tr1) Nokuro/Shutterstock.com. (tr2) Andrey_Popov/Shutterstock.com. 50 (tr1) Hans Bjurling/Johner Images/Getty Images. (tr2) SerrNovik/iStock/Getty Images. 52 (tr1) 9peaks/Shutterstock.com. (tr2) Edward Berthelot/French Select/Getty Images. 54 (tr1) Ljupco Smokovski/Shutterstock.com. (tr2) Syda Productions/Shutterstock.com. 62 tankist276/Shutterstock.com. 64 (tr1) vm2002/Shutterstock.com. (tr2) Robert Kneschke/Shutterstock.com. 66 (tr1) AlexM9/Shutterstock.com. (tr2) Geoff Robins/AFP/Getty Images. 68 (tr1) Zanna Holstova/Shutterstock.com. (tr2) The Washington Post/Getty Images. 70 (tr1) Monkey Business Images/Shutterstock.com. (tr2) wk1003mike/Shutterstock.com. 72 (tr1) Mathisa/Shutterstock.com. (tr2) Jari Hindstroem/Shutterstock.com. 74 (tr1) Thor Jorgen Udvang/Shutterstock.com. (tr2) Rawpixel.com/Shutterstock.com. 82 Monkey Business Images/Shutterstock.com. 84 (tr1) Ridofranz/iStock/Getty Images. (tr2) Blend Images - Hill Street Studios/Brand X Pictures/Getty Images. 86 (tr1) Whitemay/E+/Getty Images. (tr2) Dragon Images/Shutterstock.com. 88 (tr1) Billion Photos/Shutterstock.com. (tr2) Danil Nevsky/Shutterstock.com. 90 (tr1) Monkey Business Images/Shutterstock.com. (tr2) Zonda/Shutterstock.com. 92 (tr1) Jeremy Graham/dbimages/Alamy Stock Photo. (tr2) Jose Luis Pelaez/Iconica/Getty Images. 94 (tr1) KatarzynaBialasiewicz/iStock/Getty Images. (tr2) Antoniodiaz/Shutterstock.com. 102 Mmkarabella/Shutterstock.com. 104 (tr1)

Klaus Vedfelt/Iconica/Getty Images. (tr2) Jacek Chabraszewski/Shutterstock.com. 106 (tr1) Pavel L Photo and Video/Shutterstock.com. (tr2) Petr Student/Shutterstock.com. 108 (tr1) Goami/Shutterstock.com. (tr2) ThamKC/Shutterstock.com. 110 (tr1) Savitskaya iryna/Shutterstock.com. (tr2) Natthawon Chaosakun/Shutterstock.com. 112 (tr1) Bikeriderlondon/Shutterstock.com. (tr2a-b) Handout/Getty Images News/Getty Images. 114 (tr1) KAE CH/Shutterstock.com. (tr2) Eldar nurkovic/Shutterstock.com. 122 lzf/Shutterstock.com. 124 (tr1) Hero Images Inc./Alamy Stock Photo. (tr2) Monkey Business Images/Shutterstock.com. 126 (tr1) Tara Moore/Stone/Getty Images. (tr2) Armadillo Stock/Shutterstock.com. 128 (tr1) Rob Carr/Getty Images Sport/Getty Images. (tr2) Monkey Business Images/Shutterstock.com. 130 (tr1) DW labs Incorporated/Shutterstock.com. (tr2) Yongyut Kumsri/Shutterstock.com. 132 (tr1) S1001/Shutterstock.com. (tr2) Max Topchii/Shutterstock.com. 134 (tr1) Sergei Bachlakov/Shutterstock.com. (tr2) Bikeriderlondon/Shutterstock.com. 142 Monkey Business Images/Shutterstock.com. 144 (tr1) Alexander Raths/Shutterstock.com. (tr2) Sam Edwards/Ojo Images/AGE Fotostock. 146 (tr1) Joseph Sohm/Shutterstock.com. (tr2) untitled/Shutterstock.com. 148 (tr1) Viewimage/Shutterstock.com. (tr2) Praszkiewicz/Shutterstock.com. 150 (tr1) Wavebreakmedia/iStock/Getty Image. (tr2) Koya979/Shutterstock.com. 152 (tr1) Tetra images/Getty Images. (tr2) Robert Kneschke/Shutterstock.com. 154 (tr1) Alter-ego/Shutterstock.com. (tr2) RosaIreneBetancourt 1/Alamy Stock Photo.